'Are you serious

'You want *me* to loo
finished, a look of inc
mouth pucker.

'Is it really such a bizarre request to make, then, Angel?' Rory queried softly. 'Particularly to someone whose whole livelihood used to be caring for children?'

'Because it isn't just *any* baby we're talking about here! Surely you can see that!'

'He's my nephew—'

'And he's the son of my ex-husband!' she added acidly. 'The son he had with another woman!'

Sharon Kendrick was born in West London and has had *heaps* of jobs which include photography, nursing, driving an ambulance across the Australian desert and cooking her way around Europe in a converted double-decker bus! Without a doubt, writing is the best job she has ever had, and when she's not dreaming up new heroes (some of which are based on her doctor husband!), she likes cooking, reading, theatre, listening to American west coast music and talking to her two children, Celia and Patrick.

Recent titles by the same author:

LONG-DISTANCE MARRIAGE
THAT KIND OF MAN
MAKE-OVER MARRIAGE

THE BABY BOND

BY
SHARON KENDRICK

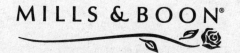

MILLS & BOON®

To Alan Stedman, who is not only the world's most
brilliant doctor—he also has the irresistible smile of
the true romantic hero!

*First published in Great Britain 1998
Harlequin Mills & Boon Limited,
Eton House, 18-24 Paradise Road, Richmond, Surrey TW9 1SR*

© Sharon Kendrick 1998

ISBN 0 263 81141 7

*Set in Times Roman 10½ on 12 pt.
01-9809-45791 C1*

*Printed and bound in Norway
by AiT Trondheim AS, Trondheim*

CHAPTER ONE

THE telephone screamed like a banshee and Angel—her dark hair drifting like smoke around her shoulders—walked along the corridor to pick it up.

'Fitzpatrick Hotel. Hello?' she said softly.

'Angel?'

Angel's heart stilled as she heard her name, the single word spoken in a voice at once so strange and yet so shockingly familiar that it struck her like a blow. Disorientated, she gripped onto the receiver, the white knuckling of her fingers the only outward sign of her distress. She opened her mouth to speak, but no words came.

There was a long pause, and then the low, masculine voice growled out the word again, so that it rang deeply in her ear. 'Angel? Angel? Are you still there?'

'Y-yes,' she gasped, her lungs feeling oxygen-deprived, her legs like lead as her memory played tricks on her. 'That—that isn't you, is it, Chad?'

'No. It isn't Chad.' The denial was emphatic, but something rather odd coloured the speaker's reply. 'It's Rory.'

Angel swallowed. Of course. Didn't they say that siblings' voices always sounded remarkably similar on the telephone?

Rory Mandelson. Chad's brother. And her brother-in-law. A man she had scarcely known, whose self-contained exterior she had never got close to penetrating, no matter how many times they had met. A man she had felt distinctly uncomfortable with, for reasons she had never quite got round to exploring—other than the fact that he had not approved of her marriage to his only brother. He had made that very plain.

And yet Rory had been the person she had turned to when she'd wanted to track down her missing husband—knowing that if anyone could find Chad then Rory could. She hadn't wanted to involve the police, unwilling to have her life put under the microscopic scrutiny that a police investigation would entail. Though she was uncertain why she'd had such blind faith in her brother-in-law.

Instinct, perhaps. The older she got the more trust she placed in instinct. And, in her more lucid moments, Angel acknowledged that maybe Rory's so-called arrogance—which Chad had complained about so often—had in fact been an unshakeable strength of character. Oh, yes—it had been all too easy to feel ambivalent about Rory Mandelson.

But that had been in another age, another life.

Now she needed to know one thing, and one thing only. Then she could go and live out the rest of her life in some kind of peace.

Cases like hers were well documented—her odd feeling of detachment nothing unusual. Why was it, Angel wondered, that those left behind by people who disappeared without trace always seemed to have a huge chunk of their life missing?

'H-have you found him, Rory?' she stumbled. 'Have you found my husband?'

Another pause, but this time a silence so uncomfortable that Angel could almost feel the awkwardness fizzing its way down the telephone wires, and she felt herself swaying with awful premonition.

Rory's voice was heavy. 'Yes, I've found him—'

'Where is he?' she demanded quickly.

There was uncharacteristic hesitation, as though he was momentarily lost for words. 'Angel, I need to see you, to talk to you—'

'Tell me!' she insisted. 'In the name of God, Rory Mandelson—will you please tell me where my husband is?'

'Angel—'

Something in the way he said her name this time forewarned her. It was a tone of voice she had heard used before, a tone which conveyed both compassion and condolence. And when someone spoke that way, it could mean only one thing....

'He's dead, isn't he?' she choked out in disbelief. 'Chad is dead?'

'Yes, he is,' he told her, more gently than she had ever heard him speak. 'I'm afraid that Chad was killed in a car crash eight days ago. I'm so very sorry, Angel.'

Dead?

The vibrant, crazy Chad Mandelson, snuffed out like a candle?

Angel shook her head frantically from side to side, so that the thick black hair beat heavily against the slender column of her neck. 'No,' she whimpered, in shocked and dazed denial. 'He can't be dead!'

'I'm so sorry, Angel,' he said again.

The part of her which wasn't frozen in disbelief wondered why Rory Mandelson of all people was offering *her* sympathy, when she was nothing more than an estranged wife. And a deserted wife to boot. A wife he had never approved of Chad taking in the first place.

She shook her head once more, as if trying to clear the fuzziness which seemed to have descended on her like a dank, oppressive blanket. Surely she should offer some words of kindness to *him.* His only brother. His last living relation. Shell-shocked, she forced her lips to utter conventionally, 'I'm sorry, too, Rory.'

'Yes.' But he clipped the word out, as though he doubted the sincerity of her condolences.

Angel swallowed, forcing herself to ask the question she knew must be asked. 'And when...when is the funeral?'

There was another pause. 'I've just come back from the funeral,' he told her, his words seeming to be drawn out of him reluctantly. 'It took place earlier today.'

'You've already *had* the funeral?' she asked, still shocked and bewildered.

'Yes.'

So. No time to pray for the repose of his soul. And no opportunity to say goodbye to her husband properly, either. For wouldn't a funeral have provided the natural and complete cutting of ties, in view of everything that had happened between them?

'I wasn't invited, then,' she observed dully.

'I honestly didn't think you would want to come, Angel. I can't think of another woman in the same situation who would have.'

'And shouldn't *I* have been the one to decide that?' she cried. 'Couldn't you at least have asked me?'

'Yes, I could.' His voice seemed to come from a long way away as he answered her accusation slowly. 'Of course I could, Angel. And you're right—I should have done. I just presumed that you would find it too—'

'Too what?'

'Too distressing. After everything that had happened between you.'

'You mean that people would have been laughing at me?'

'That isn't what I meant at all!' he growled. 'I just thought that you had been through enough with Chad, and I couldn't think of many estranged wives who would have wanted to be there—given the circumstances.'

Angel pressed her nails painfully into the palm of her hand, as if to reassure herself that she was still alive, because she felt as colourless and as transparent as a ghost. 'What circumstances?' she intoned. 'Tell me, Rory!'

'Not now!'

His words rang out powerfully, broaching no argument, and Angel remembered Chad's words drifting back to her—that what Rory wanted, Rory usually got.

'I'm coming over to see you,' he continued inexorably.

'That won't be necessary,' she answered stiffly. 'I can see little point in that *now*! And it's pointless your coming all the way to Ireland, when I can speak to you on the phone. Why don't you just rejoice that my association with your family has come to an end, that your wish has finally been granted?'

'I'm coming over to see you,' he repeated, as if she hadn't objected at all. 'I need to talk to you, Angel.'

She opened her mouth to suggest that he said whatever it was he wanted to say right now, but she closed it almost immediately. Something about the way he spoke made her realise that to argue with him would be futile, but then hadn't Chad always told her that Rory never took no for an answer. 'When?' she asked, wishing that she had the strength to put up a fight. And win.

'On Monday. I'll be with you on Monday.'

'*Monday?*' she whispered faintly. The day after tomorrow.

So soon?

Too soon, thought Angel as reality drove home with all the gritty force of a hailstorm. Too soon to take everything in.

But Rory had obviously misinterpreted her response. 'I was going to try and make it tomorrow, but everything is in chaos here. I've been busy with...' He hesitated. Angel thought she heard him swallow. 'Formalities,' he finished baldly.

She could imagine. The legal process of death. Angel swallowed too as she tried to take in the momentous news. It was unbelievable. Truly unbelievable.

She closed her eyes and remembered a long, hot summer. An Irish girl alone in London, working as a nanny in a sterile, unfriendly house. Angel had been like a fish out of water, yet unwilling to admit defeat, to return home, to her overworked mother and her six brothers who wouldn't lift a finger to help themselves.

Then the devil-may-care Chad Mandelson had entered her life like a ray of sunshine. Chad hadn't believed in problems; he'd shrugged each and every one off with that careless smile which captivated every woman around, Angel included. He'd been the kind of man who in Ireland would have been called a 'chancer', but in the hostile world of the big city Angel hadn't cared. He'd been her rock and she had clung onto him.

He'd been an ex-model and a failed actor, doted on by his ageing mother and so unlike his austere and severe older brother that it had been hard to take in that they were the same flesh and blood. When Angel had met him, he'd been recently bereaved and still grieving for his mother. Afterwards she'd wondered whether that was why he had clung to her, too. But she had answered a need in him, just as he had answered one in her.

And now he was dead.

Dead.

Angel tried to imagine the shocking reality. Dark, unwelcome thoughts began to flood into her shattered mind and she felt the telephone slip from between boneless fingers.

Hundreds of miles away in England, Rory was deafened by the sound of the receiver as it clattered onto the hard, cold slabs of the flagstoned floor.

CHAPTER TWO

THERE was a tap on the door of the old-fashioned parlour, and Mrs Fitzpatrick, the matriarch of the Fitzpatrick Hotel, peered in to see Angel sitting motionless on the sofa.

'Angel?'

Angel looked up from the photo she had been studying and tried to compose herself, though it wasn't easy. She had been feeling so emotional since hearing of Chad's death that her face kept crumpling up with disbelief, and tears were never very far from the surface. She cleared her throat. 'Yes, Mrs Fitzpatrick?'

Mrs Fitzpatrick was looking more agitated than Angel could ever remember seeing her—even more flustered than the time that the goose had flown into the parlour, minutes before the parish priest had arrived to take tea! Her thick Irish accent was very pronounced, the result of never having ventured further afield than twenty miles from the place where she had been born.

'The gentleman you're waiting on; he's here to see you now. He's just turned up in a fancy-looking motor car!' she finished, on a note of excitement which she couldn't quite hide, despite her obvious concern for Angel.

Angel swallowed nervously, and nodded. So Rory had finally arrived, had he? That would explain why Mrs

Fitzpatrick was looking so rattled—for how often did tall
barristers with heartbreakingly stern faces wander into
the Fitzpatrick Hotel? No, men like Rory Mandelson certainly didn't grow on trees in any part of the world—
least of all in this part of Ireland!

'Would you like me to show him in?' prompted Mrs
Fitzpatrick.

Angel shifted stiffly on the sofa. She hadn't known
when to expect him, so she had risen at six, just to be
sure. Still in shock, she had sat as inert as a statue all
morning waiting for him, dressed all in black, as was
still the local custom. Her thick, dark hair she had
scraped back severely with combs, but now she wondered why she had bothered. It was a style she wore
every day whilst working, but this morning her fingers
had felt useless—had shaken so much while she struggled to put the combs in place that already rogue curls
were beginning to unfurl around her neck.

'Thank you, Molly,' she answered quietly. 'Would
you mind awfully?'

'Not at all!' The older woman narrowed her eyes
shrewdly. 'And how about a drop of brandy for you,
Angelica? Bring a bit of colour back into your cheeks?'

But Angel shook her head, suppressing a shudder. It
was eleven o'clock in the morning, and she didn't want
Rory Mandelson walking in and finding her with a glass
raised to her lips. He had never wanted her to marry his
brother in the first place, but she had no desire to sink
any further in his estimation.

Since his phone call she had barely slept. She had lain
awake at night, wondering why he was even bothering

to come to see her at all—until she'd remembered that
he was a barrister, and that there was a need for him to
create some kind of order in his life, a sense of doing
the right thing—and the right thing in Rory's mind was
undoubtedly to pay his respects to the widow of his
brother. But brandy? No way! Imagine his face! 'No, I
won't, thanks, Molly.' She gave a wan smile. 'Not just
at the moment.'

'Then I'll bring him along now, shall I?'

'Would you? Thanks.'

After Molly had bustled out, Angel put the photo back
down on the side-table and clasped her hands together,
feeling more nervous than she could ever remember feeling in her life. Though why she should be so nervous of
coming face to face with Rory after more than eighteen
months, she didn't know.

Grief, probably.

Grief made you do all kinds of things, didn't it? Made
you feel vulnerable and alone, for a start. Made you
question what life was all about and wonder what you
were doing with that life. And it made you study an old
wedding photo with amazement, as if the handsome,
laughing green-eyed girl in it was a total stranger, instead of herself.

And, yes, her husband might have fallen out of love
with her, and left her without a word of explanation, but
that did not stop her heart aching for him and the terrible
waste of a young life.

The oval mirror which hung on the plain wall opposite
offered her a glimpse of her reflection if she moved her
head very slightly.

Angel grimaced. The slim-fitting black dress she wore only emphasised the washed-out pallor of her cheeks, and her eyes were shadowed from a lack of sleep. She looked a mess.

Hardly realising that she was doing it, she patted her dark hair fussily as the door swung open, and there stood Rory, his face darkening as he saw the pose she struck, and her hand fell to her side.

Now *why* had she been caught looking as though she was preening herself—something she never normally did? Why, he probably thought that all she was concerned about was feminine vanity—even at a dreadful time like this.

She blinked as she looked at him.

Angel had quite forgotten how he could simply seem to fill a room with his presence. She wondered, had he been born with that indefinable something which immediately drew the eye and the interest without any effort on his part? Some characteristic which planted itself so indelibly on your memory that he seemed to still be in the room minutes after he had left it.

Or had he learnt that from his job? As an advocate, he dominated courtrooms with his presence and his eloquence, representing the rights of the underdog. She remembered Chad's derisive expression, unable to understand why his big brother would pass up the opportunity to earn riches beyond most people's dreams. Instead, he fought cases for the poor and underprivileged—those who would normally be unable to afford a lawyer of his undoubted calibre.

And in that he could not have been more different

from his brother, for Chad had chased every money-making prospect which came his way.

Rory Mandelson was a big man, and a tall man, too—with the same kind of dark, rugged good looks as his younger brother. And yet he had none of Chad's wildness. Or his unpredictability—you could tell that simply by looking at him. Rory emanated strength and stability, thought Angel, like a great oak tree rooted deeply into the earth.

He stared very hard at her, his mouth flattening into an implacable line, which was understandable, given the circumstances of his visit. But it gave absolutely no hint as to how he might be feeling inside.

There was something very disciplined about Rory Mandelson, Angel realised suddenly. You wouldn't really have a clue what was going on behind those deep blue eyes of his, with the lush black lashes which curled around them so sinfully.

His black jeans were his only concession to mourning, otherwise—with a sweater as green as the Wicklow Mountains, which rose in verdant splendour outside the window—he looked just as casual as any other tourist. Not that there had been many tourists just lately, Angel acknowledged. It had been an unusually cruel and bleak January in this part of Ireland, with no signs of a change in sight.

'Hello, Angel,' he said softly. His navy eyes searched her face, and for the briefest second Angel had the oddest sensation of that blue gaze searing through all her defences, able to read her soul itself.

'H-hello, Rory,' she replied shakily. She got up from

the sofa slowly, with the exaggerated care of an old woman, and crossed the room until she was standing right in front of him. And only then could she sense the immense sadness which surrounded him like an aura, his grief almost tangible in the brittle silence. His deep blue eyes were dulled with the pain, his features strained with the effort of keeping his face rigidly controlled.

Angel acted on instinct.

Rising up on tiptoe, she put her arms tightly around him in the traditional gesture of condolence, and let her head fall helplessly to his shoulder, expecting him to enfold her in his arms in an answering gesture of comfort.

She would have done the same whoever it had been—man, woman or child. It was an intuitive action, and one prompted by the haunted expression in his blue eyes, but Angel felt his muscular frame stiffen and shift rejectingly beneath her fingertips, and she immediately dropped her hands to her sides, where they hung awkwardly, as if they were not part of her body but someone else's.

'I'm sorry,' she said woodenly as she glimpsed his shuttered expression. He was English, after all. Perhaps the widow of his brother should not have been flinging her arms around his neck with so much familiarity. Perhaps it was not the 'done thing'.

'Yes, I know,' he responded flatly. 'Everyone is sorry. He was too young—much too young to die.'

Had he deliberately misunderstood her? Angel wondered. Been unwilling to dwell on her action because he was embarrassed by it? Or appalled by it?

Vowing to make amends, and to act as appropriately as the circumstances demanded, she gestured to a chair. 'Would you like to sit down, Rory?' she asked him formally. 'You've had a long journey.'

He looked at the chair she had indicated, as if doubtful that it would accommodate his long-legged frame, and shook his head. 'No. I'll stand, if you don't mind. I've been sitting in the car for hours.'

'A drink, then?'

'No. Not yet.'

Their eyes met.

'Then are you going to tell me why you're here?' asked Angel quietly. 'Why you came?'

His dark head shook emphatically. 'Not yet,' he said again, and Angel decided that she had never met a man who could carry off evasiveness with so much aplomb.

His eyes were distracted by something, and he reached to the side-table and picked up the wedding photograph she had been studying before he arrived. Rory's mouth twisted as he stared down at the differing expressions of the participants, frozen in time in a group combination which could now never be repeated. 'So, you were reliving happier times, were you?' he queried, his voice hard and mocking.

'Is that so very wrong, then?' She knew she sounded stung, almost defensive. Was this what he did to witnesses on the stand—backed them into a corner until he had them lashing out, saying things they probably hadn't meant to say? 'It's one of the few photos I have of your brother.'

He shrugged. 'Forgive me if I sound cynical,' he ob-

served coolly. 'But, as you know, I never thought that
the wedding should go ahead in the first place—'

'Oh, yes, I know *that*!' she whispered back, with a
bleak laugh which was the closest Angel ever got to
feeling bitter about the whole affair. 'You made that
quite clear at the time!'

'And circumstances bore out my initial assessment of
the relationship,' he mused.

She stared at him in horror. 'You stone-hearted beast!'

He didn't bat an eyelid. 'I would therefore be an out
and out hypocrite if I now professed to approve of the
marriage simply because Chad is dead.'

Angel drew in a deep, shuddering breath as he clipped
out that cold, final word. 'Must you put it quite so *cal-
lously*?' she demanded, wondering whether he had a
sympathetic bone in his body.

His lips flattened. 'How else would you like me to put
it? Do you want me to use euphemisms for what was
essentially a horrible and violent end to Chad's young
life? He hasn't "passed on" or "fallen asleep", you
know. He's *dead*, Angel—and we both have to accept
that.'

'Are you deliberately being brutal?' she asked him
weakly.

'Yes,' he admitted, watching a pulse beat frantically
at her throat. 'But sometimes brutal is best if it makes
you face up to facts.'

Facts.

Angel sank down onto the edge of a chair without
thinking as she asked the question whose answer she had
little desire to hear. 'So wh-what happened—exactly?'

He seemed to hesitate, the blue eyes narrowing as if he was silently working out a problem. Yet when he spoke he sounded icily calm. 'His car hit the central reservation, and—' He stopped when he saw the sugar-whiteness of her skin. If he had thought that she was pale before, well, now she looked positively anaemic. 'You're not ready for this,' he said abruptly. 'You need a drink.'

'No—'

'Oh, yes, you do.' His mouth was grim. 'And so do I.'

Too weak to object, Angel watched while he located the decanter and two glasses and poured them each a large measure. If she hadn't been so shell-shocked by the whole sequence of events, then she might have told him that he had picked up the wrong glasses, and that after he had gone Molly Fitzpatrick would crucify her for not giving a man like Rory Mandelson the best Waterford crystal!

'Here. Drink this,' he instructed as he handed one to her, in that rather autocratic manner of his which had always used to drive his younger brother nuts.

Angel sipped and fire invaded her mouth as the strong liquor immediately caused her tense limbs to relax. Without realising that she was doing it, she sat back in the chair and closed her eyes. When she opened them again it was to find Rory sitting opposite her, his eyes fixed on her face. He hadn't touched his brandy, she noted.

'Are you okay?' he wanted to know.

Angel nodded. 'I'm fine now.'

'You don't look fine. You're so pale that you look as though you're about to pass out. Though that might be due to the fact that you're clothed from head to foot in black,' he added critically.

She was sensitive to the unmistakable reproof in his voice. 'You obviously don't approve of my wearing black, then, Rory?'

His broad shoulders in the green sweater barely moved, but he managed to convey all the censure of a dismissive shrug. 'Surely *my* feelings on the subject are irrelevant,' he responded quietly. 'You must wear what you see fit. Indeed you must behave in any way that seems appropriate.'

But it was clear that he considered her mourning clothes to be highly *in*appropriate! Angel put her glass down with a trembling hand. Just who did he think he *was*? Coming over to Ireland when she hadn't even wanted him to! *And* with a face like thunder! Sitting there in judgement of *her* as though she were some kind of floozie—when everyone knew that Rory Mandelson had had more women in his thirty-four years than any man had a right to have.

'Oh, I will,' she responded, with a defiant little shake of her head. 'Never you fear about *that*, Rory—but I want to know just what it is that you object to. Do you think I have no right to mourn my husband?'

His eyes narrowed sharply, so that they appeared like two bright sapphire shards which slanted beneath the ebony-dark brows. 'But he was your husband in name only, wasn't he, Angel? He disappeared from your life over a year and a half ago. The marriage vows which you made so enthusiastically ended up not being worth the piece of paper they were written on.'

She lifted her chin. 'Just as you predicted, in fact.'

His gaze didn't waver. 'Yes. Just as I predicted.'

Angel bit her lip. 'And I suppose it gave you pleasure, knowing that you were right. Knowing that all your gloomy prophecies were fulfilled. That we couldn't live together and that I drove him away. Did it, Rory?'

His eyebrows knitted together and he gave a small laugh that was totally devoid of humour. 'Did it give me pleasure? Is that what you think of me then, Angel? That my ego is so insufferably huge that I would enjoy seeing your marriage crumble simply because I had anticipated that it might happen?'

'You tell me,' she responded tonelessly.

Shaking his head with exasperation, he turned on his heel and walked across the room to the window, where the beauty of the spectacular backdrop of mountains momentarily took his breath away—something which did not happen to Rory Mandelson very often. He waited for a moment before he turned round and leaned negligently against the windowsill, and the semi-relaxed stance showed off his physique to perfect advantage.

Did he not realise, Angel wondered rather helplessly, that with his long legs stretched out in front of him like that, and his ruffled dark hair and eyes of deepest blue, he looked like most women's fantasy come to life? You would have thought that he might have the decency to wear something dull or at least something that camouflaged his body. Or was it his intention that the soft cashmere of the jade sweater should cling so lovingly to each hard sinew of his torso?

Angel shook her head slightly, recognising with a shock the path her thoughts had been leading her down. What was she *doing*, for pity's sake—drooling over her ex-brother-in-law?

Rory's mouth tightened as he registered the way she was looking at him. 'What kind of brute would I be,' he challenged softly, 'if I rejoiced in the demise of my only brother's marriage? God, Angel—is that the type of man you think I am? No, on second thought, please don't answer that!' He threw her a look which was tinged with regret. 'Once I could see that you were both determined to go through with it, then naturally I wanted to see it last.'

'But then I drove him away?' she quizzed.

He looked at her with ocean-dark eyes. 'I don't know. Did you?'

Angel shook her head violently, and a black cork-screw curl dangled in a glossy spiral by her pale cheek. 'Oh, what's the point in discussing it now? Chad is dead! He isn't coming back!' Angel's voice started to crack as she acknowledged for the first time in her life her own mortality.

For, yes, she had grown up in a remote and fairly inaccessible part of Ireland, where the existence of a close-knit and small community meant that death was less feared than in many places—and many had been the time that Angel had been to pay her respects at houses where families sat and mourned, the body lying in the parlour while people laughed and drank and cried around it—but death had never affected her personally. Like it was affecting her now.

Tears began to slide down her white cheeks. 'It's as though he never existed,' she sobbed quietly. 'As though he was never here!'

Rory frowned at her obvious distress. He had seen Angel cry only once before, when Chad had disappeared without trace and she had come—inexplicably—to him for assistance. At the time he had been resolutely un-impressed by her distress, partly, he suspected, since he had so adamantly warned her off the marriage in the first place.

But this time for some reason he found the sight of her tears unbearably moving. 'Of course he existed,' he contradicted softly, and, coming back to perch on the edge of the chair opposite hers, he took one pale, cold hand between his and rubbed at it absently with the pad of his thumb.

As physical consolation went, it was merely a crumb of comfort, and yet Angel derived an extraordinary sen-sation of calm just from the touch of his hand. She sniffed, and took the handkerchief he silently proffered and blew her nose like a child.

'You still haven't told me exactly how it happened,' she said.

For the first time since his arrival Rory looked uncom-fortable. He had rehearsed what he was going to say over and over again in the car—aloud and in his head—and yet now his pat words of explanation seemed curiously inadequate, especially when he was confronted by the sight of Angel's over-bright eyes.

He decided to try a different approach from the one he had planned. 'Tell me about the last time you saw Chad,' he instructed softly.

Angel blinked. 'But you know all about that! When he just completely disappeared like that, I came to see you.' Thinking that if anyone would be able to trace Chad, then it would be his dynamic older brother.

'But at the time you explained very little, Angel— other than the fact that he had gone,' he reminded her quietly.

Because she had felt raw and humiliated, with her confidence in tatters. Wondering just what sort of person she must be if her husband of less than a year could go off and leave her like that, without a word to anyone.

'So tell me again, Angel,' he insisted, in his deep, compelling voice. 'Only this time tell me everything.'

And, despite any reservations she might have had about discussing something as painful as Chad's departure, Angel was no exception to anyone else in responding to the force of Rory's personality. With those blue eyes boring into her like that it was impossible *not* to answer him. She focused her mind to concentrate on what he had asked her, though, to be perfectly honest, it was a relief to have something else to focus her thoughts on other than the wrenching realisation that Chad was dead.

'The last time I saw Chad he was leaving for work,' she began slowly, as she cast her mind back to that morning more than eighteen months earlier. 'I remember that it was a glorious, golden June day. The sky was blue, the sun was shining, and I was going to meet him for a drink after work that night.'

'And?'

'And nothing.' Angel shrugged. 'That was it.'

Rory's face became shuttered. 'Did he show any signs that something could be wrong?'

She frowned at him in confusion. 'Wrong?' she echoed. 'What could be wrong?'

'With the relationship,' he elaborated. 'Anything which might have indicated to you that he was planning to disappear from your life without a word?'

Angel bit her lip. With the benefit of hindsight it was easy to see that there had been plenty wrong with their relationship—but she had been so young. So green. So determined to prove wrong everyone who had prophesied disaster that she had ignored the danger signs looming large on the horizon. But she couldn't possibly tell Rory about *those*, now, could she? She couldn't really start explaining that within mere months of her marriage to his brother their sex life had not merely died down but had petered out all together.

'We weren't communicating that well,' she hedged, which she supposed was *one* way of saying it.

'But you hadn't argued?'

Angel shook her head. 'No. That was the oddest thing. We hadn't. Chad just seemed very distracted during those last few months. That's all.' She fixed him with an unblinking green stare that dazzled him with its emerald blaze. 'But that's all irrelevant, surely? Isn't it time that you told me exactly what you've found out, Rory?'

There was a fractional pause. 'Do you want me to break it to you gently?'

She cocked her head to one side and looked at him perceptively. 'Is that possible?'

'Not really, no,' he admitted reluctantly. 'He had another woman, you see.'

His words confirmed her unspoken fears. Yes. Of course he had. Some part of her had known that all along. The part that wasn't affected by her relative youth and lack of experience. The part that was passed on down through the generations and was known as a woman's instinct. The part that had registered his complete lack of desire for her whenever he had looked at her. Angel swallowed.

'He had another woman,' Rory repeated baldly, because her total lack of reaction to his controversial statement made him imagine that she had not heard him the first time.

'Yes,' said Angel, and let out a long, low sigh. 'That figures.'

'Do you want me to continue?' he questioned.

She drew her chin up proudly. 'I hope to God that I'm not the kind of person who runs away from the truth, Rory. So, yes, please continue. Tell me about this woman. Does she have a name?'

Some indefinable emotion briefly escaped from the shuttered confines of his face, hardening his mouth into a forbidding line. 'Jo-Anne. Jo-Anne Price.'

Angel wrinkled up her nose as the name struck a familiar chord in her memory. 'And she's Australian. Am

I right? She worked as a temporary at the advertising agency.'

'That's right.'

'She had just finished uni,' Angel remembered, racking her brain. 'And she had come to get work experience in England.' Angel pushed a stray strand of hair off her forehead, finding that actually she seemed to know an awful lot about a woman she had only met once or twice. So how was that? Maybe Chad had spoken about her lots, and she simply hadn't noticed. 'Hadn't she?'

Rory nodded uncomfortably. 'Yes, that's right. She had. Chad met her in a pub near the office, found her a temporary job at the agency, and, *bingo*, suddenly he was in love.'

Angel drew in a deep breath, stunned by his cruel candour, despite all her protestations that she could take whatever he had to tell her. 'And I was his bride of less than a year,' she reminded him bitterly. 'So was he not still in love with me?'

There was a small, uncomfortable pause. 'I think that Chad *thought* he loved you, Angel, and that's why he married you.' Rory's face hardened again with the pain of the truth. 'Only then Jo-Anne appeared on the scene, and...'

'And?' prompted Angel acidly, glaring at him, as though it was *his* fault.

Rory held his palms out in a gesture of apology, realising that he owed her the truth, however painful. 'He wasn't quite sure what had hit him. This wasn't just a fling, you see. It was that once-in-a-lifetime thing—if you believe it exists. I don't, personally.' His face darkened. 'But Chad certainly did.'

Angel winced.

'I'm sorry, I shouldn't have said—'

'Oh, yes, you should!' she declared fiercely. 'I told you that I wanted the truth, and that's exactly what you're giving me. And, yes, you are absolutely correct in your assessment, Rory. Chad *thought* he was in love with me—that's why he married me. And then...' But she shook her head, unwilling to pursue it further. What on earth was the point of dissecting her relationship with her husband? Especially *now*. And especially not with his big brother.

But Rory did not prompt her, or press her to continue. Instead he sat back in his seat and raised the glass of brandy to his mouth to take his first sip, then he put the glass carefully back down on the table.

'Chad couldn't face telling you what had happened. Or me, for that matter. He and Jo-Anne just took off for Australia. They wanted to get away from anyone who might cast censure on their perfect relationship. A form of geographical escape, I guess.'

'Well, not quite—since I presume that she had family living in Australia? And most parents wouldn't really want their daughter involved with a married man, surely?'

'No, you're right. They wouldn't.' Rory frowned. 'But that wasn't going to be a problem. Not in Jo-Anne's case, anyway. All her family were dead, you see. She was completely on her own, and I think that fact triggered a protective quality in Chad which he hadn't realised existed.' He gave a deep sigh, as though his next words were the hardest of all to say. 'And it meant, of course, that they had something very big in common. They were both orphans—united against the world.'

Angel's green eyes narrowed as something in his voice alerted a sixth sense in her. A sense of danger. 'There's something else, isn't there, Rory? Something that you aren't telling me?'

He gave her the kind of smile which told her she shouldn't worry her little head about anything, but Angel had grown immune to men with dazzling smiles. Immune to most men generally. Broken marriages tended to have that effect on women.

'Why don't we take this one step at a time?' he suggested silkily, but his eyes had taken on a watchful gleam.

'Because you're hiding something from me!'

He expelled the breath he had been holding. Damn the woman, and damn her intuition, too! 'Okay then, Angel,' he agreed. 'I'll give it to you in a nutshell. Chad and Jo-Anne went to Australia together and travelled around and were, by all accounts, extremely happy together.'

'And how did you find all this out?' she demanded. 'You can't have just pieced it together since Chad's death. You told me that the accident only took place...' she frowned to remember '...twelve days ago.'

This had been one of the questions he had been dreading answering. 'He wrote to me just before Christmas,' he admitted quietly.

'He did *what*?' Angel rose to her feet, her face disbelieving. 'Then why the hell didn't you tell me *then*?'

'Because he asked me specifically not to—'

'And blood is thicker than water, I suppose?'

'That wasn't why I agreed—'

'And tell me, Rory,' she cut across his words sarcastically, 'if Chad hadn't died, how long would you have kept news of his whereabouts from me?'

'It wasn't my decision to make. It was Chad's. He wanted to speak to you himself. Face to face. Not by letter.'

'But he decided to wait until *after* Christmas?' she questioned frostily. 'So why put off the moment of truth? For surely once he had seen me then he would be able to ask for a divorce.'

'He had to. He wasn't able to travel until then.'

Angel glanced at him suspiciously. 'Because?'

This was proving a lot more difficult than Rory had imagined it would, but then he had quite forgotten the impact that his sister-in-law could make with those beacon-bright green eyes of hers. God, a man could lose his soul in eyes like that... And yet it wasn't fair on *her* to pussyfoot around like this, was it? To search for polite platitudes where none would ever be appropriate.

'Because Jo-Anne was expecting Chad's baby,' he told her bluntly, ignoring Angel's shocked intake of breath as he ploughed relentlessly on. 'And she was naturally precluded from flying in the latter stages of her pregnancy. Chad wanted to come and see you in person, to ask your forgiveness for his behaviour and to request an early divorce. And he wanted me to meet my brand-new nephew,' he finished heavily.

Fragments of what he was saying began to make sense at last, and the picture that they formed in Angel's brain had connotations which made her blood run cold.

'You mean that they all came over?' she demanded in horror. 'Jo-Anne and Chad and—'

'And the baby,' he concluded, only now his words sounded as though they were steeped in something bitter that he wanted to spit as far away from him as possible.

Still standing, Angel gripped onto the arms of the chair, her fists white-knuckled with fear. 'Wh-what happened?' she whispered.

'They were on their way from the airport to my house,' he told her. 'We don't know exactly what caused the accident. The other driver *had* been drinking, but he was still within the legal limit. Chad was under the limit, too,' he added quickly, meeting the question in her eyes. 'He'd changed, Angel, I knew that much from our telephone conversation. He had become a family man, proud of his new baby—nothing would have induced him to wreck all that. He may have been jet lagged. The baby might have been crying. Who knows? No one will ever know. Not now.' A muscle began to work convulsively in his cheek, but that was the only outward sign of his grief. 'Anyway, the car hit the central reservation just beyond Heathrow Airport. Chad and Jo-Anne were killed instantly—'

Angel's heart was in her mouth. 'And the baby?'

Rory buried his head in his hands so that his face was

hidden, and Angel was suddenly filled with an unpalatable fear.

'*Rory!*' she demanded urgently. 'What happened to the baby?'

As he slowly lifted his head his features looked so ravaged with pain that Angel feared the very worst. Then he suddenly said in a bleak voice, but a voice nevertheless, which held more than a trace of hope in it, 'Somehow the baby survived. Miraculously. Without a scratch. He's fine.'

'Oh, thank God!' cried Angel, and sank back down onto her chair, not noticing the tears of relief which slid down her cheeks. 'Thank God!'

He glanced over at her gratefully, incredibly moved by her generosity of spirit. 'Thank you for that, Angel,' he said softly. And in a way her reaction justified his reasons for coming to see her. Made what he had to say next a little bit easier...

'Where is he now?' she demanded quickly.

His eyes narrowed. He was unsure of whether she meant her husband or his son, and knew that a huge degree of sensitivity would need to be employed if she was referring to Chad.

'The baby,' she enlarged. 'Where is he? And what's his name?'

'He's here with me now,' Rory told her steadily. 'I brought him with me.'

CHAPTER THREE

RORY had anticipated all kinds of reaction to the news that he had brought his infant nephew with him, but the one which he got had not even featured near the bottom of the list.

Angel sprang from her chair like a jack-in-the-box and turned on him, her face white, her eyes spitting green fire and looking so incredibly *angry* that he seriously thought that she was about to start pummelling those small fists against his chest.

'Do you mean to tell me,' she demanded, her breath coming in trembling bursts, 'that you've brought a new baby—and an *orphaned* baby, to boot—over to a strange country and then just *left* him out there, in the car?'

'Angel—'

'In the middle of *winter*?'

'Angel—'

'Just what kind of a man *are* you to have charge of a young child, Rory Mandelson?' she stormed. 'I've a good mind to report you to the authorities!'

Despite everything, Rory smiled—and it was a relief to know that he still could. It was, he realised, the first time he had smiled since the police had arrived on his doorstep with the grim news of his brother's death.

'But I didn't leave him in the car,' he objected.

'Then where is he now?'

'With Mrs Fitzpatrick.'

'With…Mrs…Fitzpatrick,' repeated Angel slowly, as though he was speaking to her in a foreign language. But didn't that make sense? Wouldn't that explain the hotel owner's rather agitated preoccupation earlier this morning—rather than the conclusion to which Angel had immediately jumped? That Mrs Fitzpatrick had been bowled over by Rory's good looks!

Nonetheless, his conduct with the baby sounded like a serious case of neglect to her. 'So you just arrived here this morning and handed the baby over to her, did you?' she quizzed, as passionately as if *she* had been the barrister instead of him. 'Just like that?'

He nodded his dark head, reluctantly impressed by her tenacity. And by her *temper*! She was much more fiery than he remembered. And far too young and beautiful to be wearing those horrible black mourning clothes. 'Pretty much,' he agreed.

'And what would you have done if she had refused to babysit for you and told you she hated babies? Or what if she'd looked like an axe-murderer?'

This time he actually laughed, and that simple, uncomplicated sound of mirth reassured Rory more than anything else could have done. For it told him that heartache—even the intense, almost unendurable heartache of a sibling's tragic and premature death—could heal eventually. And that the human spirit was a most resilient thing.

'Well, I *presumed* that you wouldn't have sought employment under an axe-murderer, Angel, though I suppose one can never tell,' he mused. 'But if I'd thought

that Mrs Fitzpatrick was unsuitable to babysit for half
an hour—or was unable to cope with the demands of a
new baby, or if I'd had any reservations about her whatsoever—then naturally I would have brought him in here
with me.'

'But you didn't want to do that?' she guessed, narrowing her green eyes as she wondered why.

'No,' he said flatly. 'I didn't.'

'Because?'

'Because I thought that it would be too much for you
to handle—on top of everything else I had to tell you.'
His face had resumed its sombre expression.

'That was very thoughtful of you,' observed Angel,
hoping that her expression didn't show the surprise she
felt at his concern for her feelings.

He shrugged his broad shoulders. 'Not really,' he murmured, and something in the husky quality which tinged
his voice made Angel feel suddenly and inexplicably
aware of him as a man, and not just as a man who had
been related to her by marriage.

She swallowed down her confusion, pushed the trou-
bling thought away. 'C-can I see him?' she asked ten-
tatively.

Again, that fleeting smile. Only this time it was like
the sun breaking free from behind a cloud, thought
Angel, before she drew herself up quickly. What on
earth was she thinking of? Just because she had been
behaving like a nun since her marriage had broken
down, that didn't mean she had to undergo a complete
personality change *now*. Fancy analysing the man's

smile when there was a poor little orphaned baby waiting!

'Of course you can see him,' said Rory softly. 'He's asleep in the kitchen. Or rather—he *was* asleep when I left him.'

'Then what are we waiting for?'

Angel led the way downstairs to the kitchen, which looked as though it was straight out of a brochure on the joys of rural Ireland. There was an old-fashioned dresser covered with many plates—some chipped—and from the range drifted a soft heat and the unmistakable smell of soda bread baking. The vast wooden table which dominated the room was scratched and carved, and carried the marks of generations of children who had written their homework on it.

And there, in the centre of the table, sat a dark blue carrycot, with a white bundle swathed inside.

Mrs Fitzpatrick had been bending over the cot, but she straightened up as soon as she heard their footsteps. Her expression wasn't just curious as she glanced from one to the other of them; she was obviously *bursting* to know why this tall, handsome Englishman had arrived with a baby, asking to see Angel.

All Angel had told her was that her husband was dead, and that his brother would be arriving to see her. Molly Fitzpatrick had planned to find out more from the brother himself, but something in Rory's eyes had cautioned her and she had refrained from asking any questions. For the time being, anyway.

'I left him on the table because I didn't want the dog licking at his face!' she declared, in her thick Irish brogue. 'The kettle has just boiled and there's soda bread cooling on the side. I'll leave you to it. I'll be changing linen upstairs if you need me, Angelica.'

'Thanks,' nodded Angel, but her attention was all on the sleeping bundle, which was mostly obscured by a snowy fleece blanket, so that she barely heard Mrs Fitzpatrick leave the room.

Angel walked over to the cot and stood silently over it, unable to see more than a tiny tuft of dark, silky hair and two sooty half-moon eyelashes which swept onto perfect pale cheeks. One little fist was clenched and visible, each finger so tiny that it would have looked more at home on a doll.

Angel had always adored babies, but this baby was her late husband's son, and despite all her mixed-up emotions concerning the ending of her marriage something stirred in her heart as she watched the barely perceptible rise and fall of the little boy's chest. How she wished that he would wake so that she could pick him up!

She glanced up to find that Rory's eyes were fixed unwaveringly on her, and she felt uncomfortable under that brief, hard scrutiny. Colour rushed vividly into her cheeks, in a way it hadn't done for years. 'W-will we wait until he wakes?' she whispered.

'Yes,' he whispered back, his eyes glittering, though he made no mention of the fact that she had been blushing in a way he hadn't seen a woman blush for a long time. 'His lungs are far lustier than you would imagine for such a little fellow. Such a tiny little fellow,' he added almost dreamily, as he gazed down at his nephew.

Angel watched the almost reluctant softening of Rory's features with something approaching astonishment. But there again newborn infants had the ability to grab your complete attention, didn't they? Even from people who never normally gave babies a second glance. There was some quality in their cry which always alerted an adult to their plight. She had learnt that from looking after her younger brothers when they were growing up—long before she went to London and became a nanny and met Chad.

And this little baby in particular would surely still be missing his mother. Only an adult with a heart of stone would fail to be moved by *that* fact. 'Will I make you some tea?' she asked Rory softly.

He nodded, seeming to come to his senses as he raked his hand rather distractedly back through his thick, dark hair. 'I'd love some tea. But first I need to freshen up. It was a long drive and the crossing was rough. Could you point me in the right direction?'

'Sure I can,' she murmured automatically, while wondering just how he could manage to look so cool and unruffled after such a long, unbroken journey *and* with a brand-new baby in tow. She frowned. Were *all* barristers as commandingly in control as Rory Mandelson appeared to be?

She directed him to the grandest bathroom in the hotel, which she hoped might appease Mrs Fitzpatrick for having let him drink out of inferior crystal! Then she set about busily making tea, her mind working overtime, running round and round in circles as she tried to take in the significance of everything that Rory had told her.

Every now and again she sent over a curious glance at the sleeping bundle in the cot, but the baby slept on and she left him to it, even though part of her was longing to see what he really looked like.

How strange to think that Chad had a son now, and that his own life would continue through that son. He must have loved Jo-Anne very much, Angel decided, with an odd sort of pang, because she remembered his reaction to her tentative query about when the two of *them* would have a baby of their own. They had been married just a month when Angel realised that they had never brought up the subject of children. Not once.

She would never forget the look on his face when she had posed her innocent question. She'd seen incredulity and then, unmistakably, sheer horror. That look had told her things about Chad's attitude to her—things which could never have been put into words simply because those words would have been too cruel to utter.

And how had she responded to Chad's reaction?

Why, in the way she had always responded to something which might cause her pain. Ignore it and it might go away.

She had never brought the subject up again.

Part of that had been embarrassment, of course. Fear that Chad might have thought her some big, old-fashioned country bumpkin—eager to become barefoot and pregnant as soon as possible. Which wasn't, of course, the modern way, but—if she was being entirely honest—had, in fact, been *her* way. And one of her reasons for getting married.

Angel had always adored babies, and it was more than

being the oldest of six; it was in her make-up. But all her adult life she had been fighting a feeling of inferiority whenever she suffered from feelings of broodiness. Because it seemed to her that a woman was made to feel inadequate unless she wanted to compete in a man's world. To work all the hours that God sent and earn far more money than was good for her.

Angel couldn't think of anything worse!

She made a pot of tea, cut and buttered several wedges of the freshly baked soda bread and placed a jar of Mrs Fitzpatrick's bramble jelly on the table. She was in the process of deciding whether or not to add a big hunk of farmhouse cheese—just in case Rory was hungry after his long drive—when she heard a snuffling sound from the carrycot, which was swiftly replaced by a raucous cry. Angel scooted across the kitchen to where the baby lay, and stood staring down at him.

The tiny scrap was yelling, already bright red in the face, and she hesitated for no more than a second before bending over to carefully pluck him out of the cot and to clutch him tightly against her chest.

The baby was hungry, yes, but perhaps he felt safe within her firm embrace, maybe he heard the reassuring drumming of her heart as she cradled him. Whatever the reason, his frantic cries lessened by a fraction, and Angel found herself speaking to him in a sing-song voice as she stared down at him.

'Hello, little fellow,' she crooned softly. 'Who's a handsome-looking baby, then?'

The baby wailed.

'Are you a handsome little fellow, then? Are you?'

she persisted quietly. 'And are you going to let me get a good look at your face, instead of screwing it all up like a prune?'

And the baby opened his eyes and looked at her.

Just for a moment—that was all it was—a moment frozen in time.

Angel found herself staring into eyes as darkly blue as the deepest ocean, and a skitter of awareness skated down her spine as she recognised that this baby might have Chad's eyes—but they were Rory's eyes, too.

Mandelson eyes.

Angel gripped the baby tighter as she acknowledged how defenceless he was, how vulnerable and frail, and she was so lost in her thoughts that she failed to hear the sound of footsteps as Rory returned to the kitchen.

In fact, the only thing which *did* alert her to his presence was the growing certainty that she was being watched, and she spun round, still holding the baby, to find Rory behind her, his eyes fixed on her with a curiously intent look. She had seen it on his face before, only this time he seemed even more watchful than usual, with an air of complete stillness about him.

'Did you mind me picking him up?' Angel found herself asking.

He shook his dark head. 'Of course I didn't *mind*, Angel. Why on earth should I? You're absolutely brilliant with babies.'

'Am I?' she asked, his approval making her feel absurdly pleased. She looked down at the soft, dark hair of the baby and felt strangely reluctant to relinquish the warm and tiny bundle. 'How do you know?'

'Well, I can see for myself,' he told her quietly. 'And Chad always said that you were the most sought-after nanny in London.'

'Did he?' asked Angel, surprised to hear that Chad had given her such unqualified praise—but that was what separation did, didn't it? Made you forget all the good bits of a relationship and concentrate on the nasty ones instead. 'Did he really?'

'Yes, he did,' he agreed, his dark blue gaze still fixed with fascination on the tiny bundle she had clasped tightly to her.

Could he see his late brother in the child? wondered Angel, ruthlessly swallowing down the tears which threatened to rise in her throat. For it would be nothing more than self-indulgence to cry now. This was Rory's grief, not hers, and she must appear strong. Chad had been no part of her life, not really, even before his tragic death.

As if on cue the baby began to scream again, his little head moving frantically as he instinctively tried to steer his mouth towards Angel's breast.

'He's hungry,' she said awkwardly, lifting her head to meet Rory's rueful gaze and wishing that the ground would open up and swallow her.

'Yes.'

She would *die* if he referred to the baby's butting and rooting frantically against her empty breast.

But he didn't. He merely gave a brief, sad smile and reached into the large holdall he had obviously left in the kitchen with Mrs Fitzpatrick. From the depths of the bag he produced a bottle of milk, in the manner of a magician producing a rabbit from a hat, and Angel's relief knew no bounds. 'I had a rapid introduction to learning how to make up baby formula,' he told her drily. 'And I'm now an expert.'

'Can I heat it for you?' she questioned eagerly, keen to push the questing baby away, even while part of her longed to cradle his head there and soothe him.

'Sure.' He raised his dark brows in query. 'Unless you want me to do it—while you hold him?'

But Angel shook her dark head reluctantly. 'I think that I'm proving a bit of a...distraction,' she finished stumblingly.

He shot a swift stare of comprehension at her flushed face. 'Yes, of course,' he said swiftly. 'Here. Let me take him.' He held his arms open and Angel carefully bent down and placed the white-swathed bundle in the crook of his elbow.

'I think he's wet,' she murmured apologetically as she took the bottle from him in exchange.

'So *that's* why you couldn't wait to off-load him,' he joked softly, and his teasing seemed to evaporate some of the tension which the hungry baby had unwittingly provoked.

'He must be desperate for his mummy,' observed Angel, trying to keep the tremble in her voice at bay. 'Doesn't he miss her like anything?'

Rory shook his head. 'Not really, no. I spoke to a child psychiatrist just after the accident. He told me that babies this young have just one thing that drives them—and that's survival. They're tough—tougher than we think. He may have missed his mother very briefly, but he's too young to have formed any kind of deep attachment to her. He just transferred his dependence onto the next stable figure to come into his life.'

'And that's you, I suppose?' she asked, as she heated up the bottle on the range.

'That's me,' he agreed evenly.

Angel tested the droplets of milk on the back of her hand for heat and realised he still hadn't told her why he had come here.

And there was something else he hadn't told her either.

The warmed bottle clutched in her hand, she turned around, her heart clenching at the sight of him holding his tiny nephew with such exquisite tenderness. It was a side of Rory she had never thought she would see—a side of him she hadn't realised existed. She had only ever seen him as her disapproving brother-in-law or—just the once—looking stunning yet formidable in the flowing black clothes he wore in court.

'What's his name?' she asked suddenly.

'Mmm?' he said absently, as though he were miles away.

'The baby's name,' she continued. 'You haven't told me what he's called.'

He didn't answer immediately, just held his hand out for the bottle and plugged it into the hungry baby's mouth, so that the only sound in the kitchen was a contented glugging and the ticking of an old clock.

Angel waited patiently. She supposed that his considered response was a direct result of his legal training. Lawyers were supposed to be measured, weren't they?

But even so—she had only asked him the infant's name—not the secret of the universe!

'I'm not sure you'll particularly want to hear it,' he said eventually.

'Good God, Rory Mandelson,' she murmured, the corners of her mouth quirking as she longed to put a smile on his face. 'What kind of a name is that?'

He tried to laugh at her attempt at humour, but it wasn't much of a laugh. In the space of a few days his whole world had been turned completely upside down, and, if he were perfectly honest, he could have done with crawling into the nearest bed and sleeping the clock right round. As if he had read his mind, the baby squawked, and Rory threw him a fond but resigned glance as he realised that there was a fat chance of *that* happening!

'He's called Charles,' he told her heavily.

'Oh?' Angel raised her eyebrows and some unaccustomed bitterness crept into her voice. 'How very egotistical of Chad to give his son the same name as himself!'

Rory shrugged. 'Maybe it isn't quite as simplistic as that, Angel,' he contradicted softly. He shifted the baby onto his shoulder and began to wind him like a seasoned expert, while Angel looked on with unwilling admiration. 'He was registered as Charles Rory, actually—and they planned to call him CR. Apparently it's very popular to call children by their initials—'

'Not in Ireland, it isn't,' interjected Angel darkly. 'And those particular initials sound like a nasty sort of test you might have in a hospital!'

Rory frowned. 'Well, of course he doesn't *have* to be CR. In fact, he doesn't even have to be Charles Rory. I mean, he can be called whatever we—' He knitted his dark brows together as he corrected himself. 'Whatever suits him. He's tiny enough not to have had time to grow used to any particular name.'

'But has he been baptised?' asked Angel sharply.

Their eyes met. 'No.'

It didn't surprise her. Chad had opposed her wishes for a church wedding as he had opposed religion in general. And Angel had been too swept up in her first experience of romantic love to have had the sense to realise the importance of such fundamental differences between them. The question was, did his brother feel the same way about marking rites of passage in a church? 'Well, what's stopping you?' asked Angel bluntly.

'You think I should have him baptised?' he questioned assessingly, his deep blue eyes narrowing as he gave the baby the second half of the bottle.

'Yes. I do.' Angel's firm reply was based on instinct, not reason. This tiny scrap had already lost a huge part of his world, so why not afford him the protection of the sacraments? 'That way you can call him anything you like—the name on the baptismal certificate doesn't have to correspond with the one on his registration. And then he can formally retain the name which his parents gave him,' she said, before adding with soft perception, 'Who knows? One day he may wish to change it back again.'

He looked at her for a moment, drawing in a deep breath, as if realising the importance of the moment.

'And if I agree to have him baptised, Angel,' Rory continued, his voice sounding so low that Angel had to strain her ears to hear him, 'then would you consider coming back to England to look after him?'

CHAPTER FOUR

ANGEL stared at Rory, so taken aback that she could scarcely draw breath.

'Are you serious?' she whispered.

'I've never been more serious in my life.'

'You want *me* to look after...' She considered saying CR, but found that she simply couldn't get the word out without wincing. 'The baby?' she finished, a look of incredulity making her soft mouth pucker.

'Is it really such a bizarre request to make, then, Angel?' he queried softly. 'Particularly to someone who is used to caring for children—whose whole livelihood used to be caring for children?'

'Well, of course it's bizarre!'

'Why?'

Oh, the crisp, incisive questioning of the professional interrogator! 'Think about it.'

'I've done nothing *but* think about it for the last two weeks, woman!' he ground out. His eyes were pained as he stared at her, and the anguish which had deepened his voice made Angel long to throw her arms around him. But she remembered his reaction when she had tried to offer comfort before, and she picked up the teapot instead, unsteadily aiming dark amber liquid into the cups.

'*Tell* me your objections!' he challenged.

'Because it isn't just *any* baby we're talking about here!' She put his cup down on the table, realising as she did so that her hand was shaking. Now why was *that*? Just because his eyes were fixed on her in that terribly intent way, making her feel suddenly and hopelessly self-conscious? Surely she wasn't as impressionable as that? She drew a deep breath. 'Surely you can see that!'

'No, indeed, it isn't just any baby,' he agreed evenly. 'He's my nephew—'

'And he's the son of my ex-husband!' she added acidly. 'The son he had with another woman!' The woman he left *me* for, she might have added, but resisted. Now was not the time for bitterness or recriminations.

'What difference does that make?'

Angel sighed. 'Because it would be extremely unconventional if I were to look after him! It would make people talk!'

Rory shook his tousled head. 'But Chad isn't your ex-husband,' he corrected pragmatically. 'Since you never went through a divorce, you are now his widow, Angel—there *is* a difference, you know. And as for people talking...well, one thing I *have* learnt over the years is that there's one thing you can always depend on. People talk. Let them.'

Oh, but he could be *so* persuasive, she thought despairingly. The soft blue blaze from his eyes could surely melt a glacier.

'Surely you can see that there would be problems if I was looking after him, Rory,' she appealed, briefly wondering if he would have the nerve to be quite so cavalier with another woman. Would he have just marched in on one of his sophisticated London friends and demanded that *she* become an instant child-minder? Somehow Angel couldn't imagine it. So did he just see her as some kind of rural innocent, to be manipulated as he saw fit?

'What sort of problems?'

She wondered was he deliberately making this difficult for her? 'You know...' she hedged.

'Not unless you tell me I don't,' he countered, still with that neutral question in his eyes which made Angel want to shake him. 'Mind-reading has never been a particular talent of mine.'

'Whatever the legalities of the situation,' said Angel carefully, determined not to rise to his sarcasm, 'the fact of the matter is that this baby...is...' She heard her voice softening in spite of her reservations and wondered what it was about her and babies. Sometimes she suspected that if she was confronted with a choice between a Hollywood hunk or a tiny defenceless baby she'd opt for the infant every time! At least babies didn't let you down.

'Is what?' he prompted gently.

'Is Chad's son!'

'So does that mean,' he mused slowly, 'that you are still so upset by Chad's desertion you simply couldn't bring yourself to look after his baby? Because it would remind you too much of the man you loved—'

'And lost?' supplied Angel acidly.

Rory shrugged as he put the empty bottle on the table and rubbed at the baby's back. 'If you like.'

Angel's eyes glittered as she watched him. 'Is that

how you see me, Rory? And how the rest of the world sees me, too? As some kind of pathetic victim—because I was deserted by my husband?'

He didn't flinch under her accusing gaze. Far from it. The look in his eyes was steady, soft—almost...Angel could have sworn that she saw *approval* there.

'No, I certainly don't see you as a victim, Angel,' he responded quietly. 'And if I did then I wouldn't have dreamed of suggesting to you that you look after this baby. Victims don't tend to make the most level-headed child-carers, you know.'

'Well, why *did* you ask me?' she queried, her eyes alight with curiosity. 'Why me, when you could have your pick of the best-trained people in England? Why some Irish girl without a qualification to her name— other than the experience of helping bring up her own brothers and then a stint as a nanny in England?'

'There's the fact that you clearly adore babies,' he told her quietly. 'That's a pretty big qualification in my book.'

Angel gave a brief glance heavenwards, so that several strands of hair shivered down her back. 'But you can't *know* that! You're only going on what Chad told you.'

'Well, I saw you for myself just now,' he observed.

'Only for a couple of minutes! That's a pretty snap judgement.'

'I observe human nature every day in my job,' he said. 'And I'm practised enough to know when someone is being genuine.' He looked up, and Angel was caught in the blazing blue fire of his eyes. 'You were miles away when I walked into the kitchen a little while back and saw you cradling him against you. You had no idea that you were being observed, and yet there was no disguising the fact that you have a genuine regard for babies. And this baby in particular. You'd make a wonderful mother.'

'Why—thank you, Rory,' gulped Angel, glowing in his unexpectedly warm praise. And she almost allowed herself to bask in it—until she remembered that this was the man who had actually tried to stop her marrying Chad.

He had called round to see them at Chad's flat one evening and had accepted their invitation to supper, complimenting Angel on her spaghetti and insisting on buying a superb bottle of wine to accompany it. Angel had thought that the evening had gone very well. Until Rory had risen to leave, and had looked at them both, saying, in a cool, oh-so-controlled voice, 'If you want my advice—which you probably don't—then I'd advise against marriage at this stage. I mean, why bother?'

Angel had been outraged.

And Rory's opposition had only seemed to fire up Chad's determination to go through with the wedding.

Angel looked at Rory now and asked him a question she should have had the courage to ask at the time. 'Why were you so opposed to the marriage, Rory?'

'Angel,' he sighed. 'Must we?'

'Yes! We must!' she retorted. 'You can't honestly expect me to give your suggestion about looking after the baby any serious thought unless we do! Not if there's something as big as *that* between us. And I want to *know*! What didn't you like about me? The fact that I was a simple girl from the Bogs of Ireland? Unable to pick up the right knife and fork at the dinner table?'

'Angel Mandelson,' he growled darkly. 'If I weren't holding this baby, I honestly think that I would get up off this chair and *shake* you for saying such foolish things!' He began to unpop the poppers on the baby's sleeping suit. 'It wasn't a question of not liking *you*— my concern was your relationship with my brother. And—if you must know—I disapproved of the marriage because I thought that you were fundamentally unsuited.'

'On what grounds? You'd only met me on a handful of occasions!'

'True. But I knew Chad better than most—knew how fickle he could be. And I also knew that Chad had been spoiled rotten by our mother, and that consequently he was suffering from the ''must have'' syndrome.'

'And just what is that?' queried Angel, intrigued.

Rory shook his head. 'Forget it.'

'No way!' She laughed hollowly. 'You can't dangle a carrot like that in front of me and then tell me to forget it!'

'You won't like it,' he warned.

Her emerald eyes sent out green sparks. 'But I'm a big girl now, Rory,' she told him truthfully. 'I can take it.'

'I think he wanted to marry you because you were unobtainable.'

'But that doesn't follow!' Angel frowned. 'How *could*

I have been unobtainable when I had agreed to marry him?'

'Because I believe that there were conditions to your agreeing to marry him,' he murmured astutely. 'Weren't there?'

Angel went very still. 'What do you mean?'

Rory's mouth had thinned into a narrow line. 'I told you that you wouldn't like it—'

'Just *tell* me!'

'I suspect that you refused to have sex with him until you were legally bound together, and I think that Chad probably saw that as the ultimate prize—one of the few things that money can't buy,' he finished reluctantly.

Angel piled three heaped teaspoons of sugar into her tea, which was three more than she would have normally had, but she knew well enough the treatment for shock, and shock was what she was reeling from right now! She slowly stirred it round and round in silence until it had cooled, and it was only when she had drunk half the tea in her cup that she turned to him, the deep hurt she felt deadening her green eyes.

'Chad actually told you *that*?' she quizzed shakily, dizzy with disbelief that he could have betrayed something so intensely personal.

Rory shook his head. 'No. He didn't.'

'So if Chad didn't tell you that I was a virgin, then how could you possibly know? Share some of your secrets of human observation with me, Rory.'

His mouth twisted into a wry line, and he seemed to hesitate before speaking. 'I am never normally at a loss for words,' he told her drily, 'and this isn't a subject I would usually explore in depth—but, since you asked, I'll tell you. Your innocence was as obvious as the sun rising in the sky—it shone around you like a bright aura, if you must know.'

Which was a rather flattering way of putting it, Angel conceded grudgingly.

'And it was rare for a woman of your age to still be so innocent—'

'But I was twenty!' Angel expostulated.

'Still rare,' he murmured. 'Certainly amongst the women that Chad—or I, for that matter—was in the habit of meeting.'

Now she *was* confused! 'But if that was the case, then why did you object to the marriage, Rory? Surely if your guess was correct, and your brother's wife *did* possess such innocence, then that could have only been an admirable quality?'

He shook his head. His brother was dead. What good would it do now if he explained how he had felt about Chad's marriage to Angel? That something very precious was about to be despoiled. A treasure plundered without true appreciation of its beauty.

'I just didn't think that you were compatible,' he told her deliberately.

'I see.'

'And I was right,' he added, matter-of-factly. 'Wasn't I?'

'Yes, you were right.' She stared at him very hard. 'And yet you still want me to drop everything and come to England with you and help bring up your nephew. Now, why is that, I wonder? Why don't you go to one of the many reputable nanny agencies in London and find yourself someone who will just do the job and not cause you any grief?'

A flicker of a smile hovered about his lips. 'Why? You're planning to cause me grief, are you?'

But she deliberately steeled herself not to respond to this sudden onslaught of charm. 'You know what I mean, Rory,' she said stubbornly. 'Answer the question.'

He absently stroked the baby's crown. 'Okay. I'll tell you. I want you, as I said, because you love children, but the main reason is because I think that you would be kinder to this baby than most.'

'You mean because I was married to his father?'

'That's exactly what I mean.'

'And what about my life here?'

Rory looked around the big, old-fashioned kitchen. It was warm and homely, with the smell of baking lingering enticingly on the air, while Angel stood like a wraith in the centre of it all—dead pale against the black of her mourning clothes. He frowned deeply. It was all so wrong, somehow—to lock her youth and her beauty away in some God-forsaken place like this. And while he might be looking to her to rescue him, might he not just rescue her from such an empty fate at the same time?

'*What* life here?' he demanded brutally. 'You ran back to Ireland when your marriage broke up—but to what? Growing old before your time, carrying trays of tea to tourists? Running errands around the hotel? Seen as a failure—as a bitter woman whose husband ran off and left her? Is that what you want for the rest of your life, Angel?'

Put like that, his words sounded so cruel.

And so true.

Mortification made her retaliate. 'But I'm not just a woman whose husband has deserted her, am I?' she demanded hotly. 'Not now. Not now that Chad is dead. As you so rightly pointed out—I'm a widow, Rory. Won't that give me the respect that you imply I lack?'

If she had expected even a little bit of sympathy, then none was forthcoming. 'The fact that you're now a widow is purely academic,' he told her dismissively. 'It's just a word, that's all—a word you will no doubt use to hide behind. And it's a very powerful word, Angel, make no mistake about that. Some women use it as a protective shield to keep the rest of the world a safe distance away. And that's what I predict will happen if you stay here.'

His words had the sting of truth, but still she fought him. 'Well, just what is this marvellous alternative that you're offering me?' she declared. 'A baby this young needs *constant* attention, you know—he can't just be picked up and put down on a whim. He needs a steady influence—anything else just wouldn't be fair. And whoever looks after him is going to form a pretty strong attachment to him, and he to her.'

'Well, that's okay—'

But she shook her dark head impatiently. 'And you're *how* old?'

He frowned. 'Thirty-four. But what the hell has that got to do with it?'

Angel flattened her lips into a determined line. 'Are you married?'

'Of course I'm not *married!*' he exploded. 'I'd hardly be here throwing myself on your mercy if I had a wife at home, would I?'

'So what happens when you meet the woman of your dreams and *do* decide to settle down? A new woman won't want to share either you *or* the baby with anyone else. And why should she? She'll want him to be *her* baby, won't she?' Angel could envisage all too well the heart-rending scene of having to leave a baby you had come to think of as your own. 'So then I'd be kicked out.'

As soon as the words were out of her mouth, she regretted them. She was making herself sound like some waif and stray. Like a victim—and hadn't she promised herself, and him, that was one role she was never going to play?

'No!' He shook his head. 'Now it's your turn to listen to me, Angel. No one can look into the future and predict what is going to happen, and I don't intend to try. All I can do is assure you that I intend to share the responsibility of bringing up this baby, and if that means reducing the hours I work, then so be it.' His mouth hardened into a grim line. 'And as for finding the woman of my dreams—'

'Yes?' she prompted a little hesitantly, as she saw the cold, hard twist of his mouth.

'I've been around a little too long to believe in fairy tales like finding lasting happiness with one woman,' he ground out, and Angel didn't even realise that she had been holding her breath waiting for an answer until she expelled it in one long hiss.

If he heard, he made no comment, just pulled open the last popper of the pale blue sleeping suit and gingerly prodded at the baby's nappy. 'I need to bath him and change him,' he stated matter-of-factly. 'And while I'm doing that I'd like you to mull over my suggestion and let me know your answer. Whatever you decide, I'd like to sail for England tomorrow. And in the meantime...' The baby opened his eyes then, and Rory paused mid-sentence as he gazed down at him.

Angel saw a whole range of emotions crowd the rugged strength of his features as he stared at his tiny nephew.

She saw regret and pain and sorrow, yes, but mostly she saw love, and it was the love that swung it for her. He really loved this baby, she realised, with a grudging admiration. He wanted the very best for this baby. And how many single men of his age and with his kind of career would take on an awesome responsibility like that?

'In the meantime...' he repeated slowly, but he was still mesmerised by the baby's dark blue eyes, almost identical to his own.

'In the meantime...' echoed Angel slowly, as she picked up the holdall from the floor, and something in her voice made him stand stock-still and look at her.

'What?' he whispered, an unmistakable question in his eyes.

She returned his steady gaze with one of her own, aware of the sudden relaxing of his tense, broad shoulders and realising that he was having no trouble at all interpreting her body language. He knew very well that he had achieved what he had set out to do! Was she really that transparent, or was he just exceptionally perceptive?

Her voice was very soft, and more than a little rueful as she wondered just what she was letting herself in for. 'Well, we still haven't decided what to call him, have we?'

CHAPTER FIVE

THE countryside sped by in a blur of different greens—
the old song said there were forty shades, but Angel
could count at least a hundred.

Here and there the occasional grey of a stone cottage
loomed up and seemed to blend with the sky. It was a
cold and bleak day, the landscape bare and harsh, and
they did not see a single person out braving the brittle
bite of the wind. Angel shivered, despite the car heater
which was blowing warm air straight into her face.

She stared straight ahead, wondering just what lay
ahead of her. Rory had been so quiet since they had set
off from the Fitzpatrick Hotel, and she guessed that a
grief reaction had set in now that he had accomplished
what he had come to Ireland to do.

But grief didn't come in a constant flow, it came in
waves—sometimes they were tiny ripples which made
you feel uncomfortable and sometimes they were huge
breakers, which rocked the foundations of your being.

She glanced over and saw the rigid mask which had
frozen his features. A breaker, she decided.

She had packed her belongings in under an hour, seeing little point in hanging around at Fitzpatrick's until
the following day. She had foreseen the difficulties of
trying to forge a new relationship with the baby *and* with
Rory, especially under the watchful and rather protective

eyes of the community in which she had been living for the past eighteen months. It would have been like living under a microscope!

So, with Mrs Fitzpatrick's cautious blessing, she had left the hotel which had been her haven since her marriage had fallen apart, and taken a job in England on the strength of a heartfelt appeal from a man who was the undoubted master of verbal manipulation. And here she was now—wondering whether she would live to regret her impetuous decision!

She hadn't even phoned her mother to tell her of her abrupt change of plans. She was still plucking up courage to do that, if the truth were known. Not that her mother was a tyrant, who tried to influence Angel's life more than any other mother did—she just wasn't sure what her reaction would be when she learned that Angel had resumed close contact with the Mandelson family.

Her family hadn't liked Chad, not a bit—even before he had run off and left her. Her mother had complained that he had a weak handshake and wouldn't look her in the face properly. Who could blame them if they thought that Rory was cast from the same mould? She suspected that she would hear a good deal about leaping from frying pans into the fire—and Angel didn't think she was up to listening to that. Certainly not today.

The car purred through the narrow lanes, and Angel kept her eyes fixed to the road. It wasn't easy. In fact it was damned difficult, and it was as much as she could do to prevent her gaze from drifting over to the man next to her in the driving seat. But maybe that was normal. For who *wouldn't* stare, in the circumstances?

She hadn't seen Rory for a long time, and she was travelling back to England with him. These were reasons enough to be drawn to those hard, flinty features, Angel tried to convince herself. And her fascination had absolutely nothing to do with the way that a lock of dark hair flopped so enticingly onto his forehead—the only outward hint that maybe Rory Mandelson was not as inwardly controlled as he appeared.

With an effort, Angel dragged her attention back to the reason why she was here in the first place and glanced over her shoulder, her face automatically softening.

In the back of Rory's Bentley, the baby was sleeping like—well, like a baby! A baby, moreover, still without a name. Angel racked her brains, as she had been racking them since she had heard that the infant was to be called CR! 'How about Fergus for a name?' she suggested.

Rory turned his mouth down. 'Don't like it,' he said immediately. 'I went to school with someone called Fergus and he was the class creep. Oh, Lord! What do we have here?'

Ahead of them, a large black-and-white cow had positioned itself slap-bang in the middle of the narrow country lane, blocking it completely. With a sigh, Rory slowed the car down and braked.

'It's called a cow, Rory,' said Angel, trying not to giggle as she saw his fingers begin drumming impatiently on the steering wheel. 'They have four legs and a set of udders and provide milk and cream for the population in general. Some people enjoy eating their flesh, too, particularly roasted, on a Sunday, with a big feed of vegetables on the side. Very useful creatures, in fact, and certainly not to be glowered at like that!'

'Oh, ha ha! Very funny,' he remarked, shooting her a sideways glance and realising that she looked remarkably at ease, almost relaxed. She had always seemed slightly nervous around Chad. A good omen, he thought, his heart lifting a little. 'So how the hell do we go about shifting it?'

'You can get out and try slapping it on the rump,' replied Angel doubtfully, wondering why driving along a lane she had driven along a thousand times before should suddenly seem like the greatest adventure of her life. It said a lot about her life, really.

He threw the animal a dubious look. 'Is that what one of the local men would do?'

Angel shook her head. 'You *must* be joking! They'd retire to the nearest bar and wait for it to move itself.'

'And what if they were in a hurry?' he asked, frowning.

'This is Ireland we're in, Rory—not the middle of London!' she scolded. 'If your journey couldn't wait— you'd either shift the beast or turn the car round and choose an alternative route.'

'And which shall we do?' he mused.

'That depends. Are we in a hurry or are we not?'

Rory shrugged and became aware of the tension at the back of his neck. He had just naturally assumed that they *were*. And why wouldn't he? His whole life had been spent hurrying, and like all habits, it was a difficult one to break. 'Well, we *do* have a catamaran to catch,' he pointed out.

'When?'

'Tomorrow. From Rosslare.'

'Well, then!' She turned to him in triumph. 'It would do the baby an enormous amount of good to be out of this wretched car for a while. Speaking of which—I absolutely refuse to keep calling him "the baby". So, since you've already rejected every single name I've thought of, can you please come up with something of your own?'

He rubbed his chin and Angel looked at him expectantly. 'Well?'

There was a pause. 'Lorcan,' said Rory suddenly.

'Lorcan?' she repeated slowly.

'That's right. My best friend at law school was called Lorcan. Do you like it?'

Angel turned round to look at the sleeping child, at the two dark arcs of his eyelashes which swept the pink and white innocence of his baby skin. She tried the word over in her mind.

Lorcan. It was nothing like Charles, or Chad, or the dreaded CR! So there would be no sad memories evoked every time someone said it.

Lorcan. It rang a bell, somewhere deep in her subconscious. It was different, yes, but then so was this baby—different in that he had no parents. And what had she been taught at school by one of the kindly old nuns, long dead now? That there was nothing wrong with being different. On the contrary—differences were what made the world such an interesting place.

Lorcan. 'Yes, I do like it. I like it very much,' she told him softly, unprepared for the swift smile which lit up his face in a way she'd never seen him look before. Something outside her control made her heart lurch painfully in response. 'Wh-what does it mean?' she asked quickly, but more in an effort to distract herself than an immediate desire to know.

'I have absolutely no idea.' He shrugged. 'But I'm pretty sure it isn't rooted in something sinister—names never are. And my friend Lorcan went on to become a district attorney, which is a pretty good omen.' Omens again. That was twice he had thought of that word in the space of minutes. Maybe his brother's death was responsible for him feeling so superstitious today. 'Is that what we should call him, then, Angel?'

The word 'we' scorched its shape onto her mind, as if it had been branded there. 'Yes, I think we should,' she agreed slowly, thinking that she really mustn't read anything into warm, inclusive questions like that last one. Theirs was a working relationship, both strengthened and complicated by the fact that she had been married to his brother. It *would* be more intimate than any working relationship she had previously enjoyed, of course it would—but only up to a point.

Why, Rory had told her that he wasn't married, so no doubt he would have girlfriends galore, popping in and out of his house as the whim took them. He would probably disappear into his bedroom with them, and they would be there for hours on end—performing the sexual gymnastics that these fast London men and women were famous for!

Or maybe he *was* a one-woman man, searching for the woman of his dreams, despite all his protestations to the contrary. He probably wanted some highly intelligent and stunning super-model type to grace his side at legal functions. A bimbo with brains, perhaps.

And if she wanted any peace of mind—then she was just going to have to learn to distance herself from that area of his life.

The baby stirred and Angel smiled. 'Hello, Lorcan,' she whispered softly, and sensed, rather than saw, Rory was watching her. But she didn't look up to meet his gaze; she didn't dare. The last thing she wanted was to start concocting all kinds of romantic fantasies about him—and that sort of thing could happen all too easily when you had been living the sterile kind of life that she had been living for so long!

She was still far too vulnerable around men—that had been Chad's legacy to her—and especially vulnerable to a man as outrageously masculine as this one. Especially when he was sitting within touching distance and was the possessor of a body more suited to a man starring in a diet cola commercial, instead of a city lawyer. Mrs Fitzpatrick had said as much when Angel had told her that she was going away with him.

'You're very quiet.' Rory's deep voice interrupted her reverie.

'I was just thinking about something Mrs Fitzpatrick said when I told her I was leaving.'

'You didn't leave her in the lurch?'

Angel shook her head. 'Oh, no. Not at all. It's totally quiet in January. She kept me on in winter more as a favour, really—knowing that I'd repay her a hundredfold in the busy holiday season.'

'But she didn't want you to come away with me?' he ventured astutely.

Angel smiled. 'Didn't she, Mr Lawyer?'

'Well?' he pressed.

'I think she could see that it was a good opportunity for me,' hedged Angel.

'But?'

'I didn't say but,' she pointed out.

'It's what I call an invisible word,' he parried. 'The kind of word that hangs on the air and doesn't need to be said. Come on, Angel, tell me about Mrs Fitzpatrick's reservations—she was bound to have some.'

He was right, of course. Angel remembered the matriarch's warning, when she had sought a word alone with her to ask if she minded her going, and so soon.

'Mind?' Mrs Fitzpatrick had declared. 'Of course I don't mind! Sure, isn't it a pleasure to see a bit of life in your face for a change? You shouldn't waste your youth in a place like this—and the little fellow couldn't have anyone better to look after him than you. I've seen you with children myself—and you have a rare gift with them.'

She had paused then, and her eyes had grown very serious. 'But I'll tell you something for nothing, Angel Mandelson—I've lived a lot longer than you and I've seen enough of men to know that he's the kind of man who'll break your heart if you're not careful!'

'Oh, I'll be *very* careful,' Angel had defended herself instantly. 'And anyway, there's nothing *remotely* like that between us! It's strictly business.'

'It's never strictly business between a man and

woman!' Mrs Fitzpatrick had retorted darkly. 'Especially if they're both single. I take it he *is* single?'

'So he tells me.' Angel had smiled back, still feeling on a high as the knowledge dawned on her that you often didn't realise you were in a rut until you got the chance to escape from it. And her chance had come in the unlikely shape of Rory Mandelson and his orphaned nephew.

'You're not going to tell me what she said, are you?' said Rory finally.

'No, I'm not,' answered Angel sweetly. 'I'll leave you to make your own deductions. And if I were you I'd come to some sort of decision about where we're going—because we still happen to be blocked in by a cow.'

Rory looked at her. Then at the baby. Then at the cow, who was gazing through the windscreen at them solemnly. And as the absurdity of the whole situation hit him he laid his head down on the steering wheel and began to laugh softly.

'And what's so funny?'

He shook his head, exhausted. 'Nothing. Everything. Oh, Angel, isn't it bizarre how your life can change in the beating of a heart?'

He lifted his head and Angel saw that the laughter lines by his mouth had been deepened by strain, and that the deep sapphire eyes were shadowed by lack of sleep.

'Turn the car around!' she told him.

'What?' he frowned.

'We're not driving to Rosslare, not tonight. There's a hotel a couple of miles back down from the crossroads,' she told him. 'We can stay there for the night. And we're not in a hurry—you just admitted that yourself! Come on, Rory—agree that it makes a lot more sense for us to stay the night here and crack on in the morning!'

'Well, I'd like to press on,' he said stubbornly. 'We have a long way to go. I'd rather put up near Rosslare— at least that way I could get a lie-in in the morning.'

'Well, I think you're mad.'

'Oh, do you?' he queried softly.

Judging by the sparks being emitted by those dark blue eyes, he clearly wasn't used to receiving orders— or maybe just not from a woman! But suddenly Angel didn't care.

She had once walked into a marriage with her eyes half closed, and when it had disintegrated she had vowed that from that day on she would be true to herself. Not that she had any intention of becoming the kind of woman who 'always knows best', but no longer would she be overruled by a man simply by virtue of the fact that he *was* a man!

Especially, if, as now, he was a man so exhausted by the most unbelievable chain of events, combined with lack of sleep, that he must be barely capable of thinking straight. And also—Angel ran a practical eye over the lean contours of his cheekbones—a man in need of a good square meal. Or three.

'You have a tiny baby in your charge,' she told him. 'You aren't fit to drive all the way to the port, and what's more—you know it!'

'Okay.' He withdrew the keys from the ignition and dangled them in front of her in a glittering metal shoal. '*You* drive!' he challenged stubbornly.

Angel glared, aware that he had backed her into a corner. 'I don't.'

'Don't?' His eyebrows shot up. 'What do you mean, you don't?'

A curse on him and his barrister's precision for language! 'All right then, I *can't*,' she emphasised sardonically.

'Ah!' he observed triumphantly, his voice an unintentionally silky caress. 'So I have you completely in my power, do I, Ms Mandelson?'

Their eyes met for a long moment and as they stared at one another a silence grew and enveloped them in a heady cocoon. Angel felt her throat constrict as she became aware of her body reacting to his closeness, to that curiously intent expression in his eyes which made him look like some sexy predator.

She had never been quite so aware of the sound of the blood rushing to all her pulse points—her heart felt as though it was about to burst in her chest as she struggled to catch her breath.

'Shall I teach you?' he queried softly.

She stared at him in confusion, wondering what the hell he was talking about. 'T-teach me what?'

He raised his eyebrows. 'Why, to drive, of course, Angel—what did you think I meant?'

'Are you or are you not going to take me to the hotel?' she asked him furiously.

'And if I'm not?'

'Then you find yourself someone else to look after Lorcan,' she stated, aware even as she said the baby's name that she had no intention of following through with her threat. As she knew deep down that Rory had no intention of allowing her to either. Even if it meant bowing to common sense and doing what she had suggested all along...

'Looks like you've got me beaten.' He sighed dramatically as he put the key back in the ignition and the engine sprang to life.

'Looks that way,' she agreed, trying not to appear *too* pleased with herself! 'Now, turn the car around,' she told him firmly. 'Only not too noisily—after all, we don't want to frighten the cow!'

He was still laughing as he obeyed her instructions and drove back up the pitted lane towards the hotel.

CHAPTER SIX

'AND besides,' said Angel, 'the Black Bollier is famous around here. It would be a pity if you went away without seeing it.'

'Extraordinary name,' murmured Rory.

'An extraordinary man runs it. An Englishman,' she added, as though that explained everything. 'See. Here we are.'

The Black Bollier Hotel was a weather-beaten building with a colourful past and of sufficiently idiosyncratic appearance to appeal to a large number of tourists, especially Americans. Angel's own parents had visited the place when her father had still been alive—which wasn't that surprising as they had lived only fifty miles away—but, even so, its fame had spread far beyond County Wicklow. Even in a country like Ireland the place was renowned for the eccentricity of its owner!

It was celebrated for being 'quaint' and it was impossible to get a room during the high season unless you had had the foresight to book six months in advance. What attracted the legions of guests were reputedly the most comfortable beds in all Ireland, and an inspired menu provided by an unpredictable but technically perfect chef.

During winter months, however, apart from at lunch and dinnertime, it was reclaimed by locals whiling away

74

the long hours and waiting for something of excitement to happen. And the sight of the girl from Fitzpatrick's with a strange Englishman and a tiny unknown baby in tow was obviously all the excitement they needed.

Angel didn't know what kind of reaction she had expected when the three of them made their entrance, but it had not been the distinctly disapproving silence which greeted them. And you would have needed a heart of granite not to have felt embarrassed by the judgemental looks on the faces of the regulars.

She knew that Rory had been right, and she shouldn't *care* what other people thought of her, but who in their right mind wouldn't have been affected by such a sour reception? She half wondered whether she ought to stand in the middle of the bar to announce that she *wasn't* running off with a total stranger!

'This way,' she hissed to Rory.

'Why are you whispering?'

'Why do you think?'

'Because we're not exactly being overwhelmed by a warm reception?' he asked drily.

'Exactly. Let's just go and register.'

Angel walked through the pin-drop silence of the bar and out to the elongated cubbyhole which passed as a reception area, with Rory close behind her, carrying Lorcan.

At the reception desk sat Alan Bollier, the owner, who was busy flicking through a catalogue listing French wines.

Alan was the infamously eccentric Englishman who had the reputation locally of being a legend in his own lunchtime! As a young man he had fallen passionately in love with Ireland, working every hour under the sun until he had accumulated a tidy sum of money. Eventually he had saved enough to buy up the local hotel, and, in an astonishing display of conceit, had removed the name which had hung there for centuries and styled it after himself!

For some odd reason this had only endeared him to the locals, and they supported him in his many money-spinning ventures, which ranged from 'Haunted Hotel' weekends—which were particularly popular with Dutch tourists—through to the occasional leprechaun-spotting convention and Irish dance, or 'ceilidh'.

He was known to be a forthright man with strong opinions, and he was staring at Angel now with a decidedly unwelcoming look on his face.

'Can I help you?' he asked frostily.

'You must be Alan Bollier,' smiled Angel.

'I am,' came the stony response.

'Well, it's just great to be here, Mr Bollier. I've heard how wonderful your hotel is,' said Angel, laying on all her best Irish charm, even though his face looked about as welcoming as rain at a picnic. 'And now I've seen it for myself, I can tell that every word I heard was true!'

'Can you now?'

She decided to abandon the friendly overtures—clearly Mr Bollier was even more eccentric than he had been painted! 'Er—we'd like a room, please,' said Angel, with a nervous smile when she realised he must be leaping to all the wrong conclusions. 'I mean—we'd like *two* rooms, please.'

'That'll be two rooms next-door to one another, I suppose?' asked the patron suspiciously.

'Is there some kind of problem with that?' queried Rory pleasantly, although quite frankly he felt like asking the man if he was moonlighting for the Spanish Inquisition.

Alan Bollier met his eyes. 'And why would I have a problem with that? It's your life. You must do as you see fit. It's none of my business.'

'Quite so,' clipped Rory, not quite so pleasantly.

Angel threw Rory a look as she began to fill in the form that Alan Bollier had placed in front of her. The last thing they needed was for him to take against them—for she had neither the inclination nor the energy to go searching for alternative accommodation. And they wouldn't find accommodation as good as this without a long drive ahead of them. 'What time do you serve dinner?' she asked politely.

'Seven o'clock sharp!' he grunted, withdrawing two sets of keys and dumping them unceremoniously on the counter in front of them. 'Last orders taken at nine-thirty. And the chef won't wait—he has a home to go to, you know! Here—follow me!'

Angel and Rory followed him upstairs, where Rory's irritation evaporated as soon as he saw where he'd be sleeping. The bedrooms were wonderful in a way that only very old-fashioned Irish hostelries *could* be, he thought, with big, high bedsteads and a fire already lit and flickering warmly in the grate. He looked at the high bed with the longing of the truly weary.

'Proper sheets and blankets,' he commented approvingly, once Alan Bollier had gone. He looked around the smaller of the two rooms with unfeigned pleasure. 'I'll take this room, Angel.' He stifled a yawn and tested the mattress with his hand. 'A feather mattress, too! Wow! I haven't slept in a bed like this for years!'

'Well, of course—there's none of these duvets that you're all so fond of over there!' said Angel, as she looked at the linen sheets and silk-padded eiderdown.

'"Over there" being England, I presume?' he teased.

'Where else?'

'Hmm. I can see that we're going to have a complete overhaul on the domestic front when you arrive,' said Rory, and he put Lorcan's carrycot on the middle of the bed.

'Lord, but that Alan Bollier was as miserable as sin, wasn't he?' asked Angel, frowning.

'I don't suppose he gives everyone that welcome,' commented Rory drily. 'I mean, eccentricity is one thing—but if he always gave out the big freeze like that he wouldn't have any customers left.'

'Oh, I wouldn't be too sure about that,' Angel shook her head. 'He's *hugely* popular around here—people come from miles around to stay here. And aren't there places in London and New York where you pay for the privilege of being insulted?'

'Not quite in the same way.' He smiled. 'I suppose he knows you? Would that explain it?

'He probably knows *of* me,' said Angel. 'Everyone knows everybody else's business around here.'

'Well, then—that's why they're all being so protective

of you, and that explains the frosty reception when we arrived. What's the matter—don't you like that?'

'I'm not sure that I do, not any more,' she answered slowly. 'The close-knit community thing was what drew me back, and it was just what I needed after London. But if you're single, it can be cloying. I don't think I'll miss it too much. It's intrusive.'

He smiled. 'The way they probably see it is that you've already been deserted by one scoundrel Englishman—and now you waltz in here with another one who's about to have his wicked way with you!'

Angel opened her mouth wide, not sure how to reply to that, when there was a raucous wail from inside the carrycot.

Rory smiled at her transparent embarrassment. 'Well, there you go!' he murmured. 'Saved by the baby. So—' his eyes glinted with amusement '—shall I reserve my ravaging for later?'

Angel set her lips into a straight line, unsure of how to respond to such blatant sexual teasing. It was good to see him smiling, yes, but surely it wasn't appropriate behaviour from a man who had just lost his only brother?

She took a bottle of milk from the holdall and held it up in front of her like a shield. 'Do you want to go down and heat this up, or shall I?'

'Here, give it to me. I shan't subject you to any more of the landlord's ire!' He took the bottle from her with a sardonic smile. 'And wipe that terrified expression off your face, for goodness's sake! I'm not some black-hearted seducer, you know! Propriety will be observed,

Angel,' he added. 'You have your room and I have
mine.'

Odd how you could be both relieved *and* disappointed
at the same time, Angel thought guiltily. 'And where
will Lorcan sleep?' she queried.

There was a pause then, and his eyes flickered over
the restless shape of his nephew. 'He'd better come in
with me tonight,' he said.

Angel hesitated. She wondered if Rory had had to
comfort his tiny nephew in the dark hours before dawn,
when the night seemed endless. 'Did he cry very much
when…when…?'

'When his mother was killed, you mean?' Rory swallowed down the bitter taste in his mouth and shook his
head. 'Not very much, no. The…the ambulancemen said
that he just seemed stunned and very, very quiet—
though that could just have been the impact of the col-
lision, of course…'

Rory's words tailed off as Lorcan began to grizzle,
and instinctively they both looked up and smiled into
each other's eyes. Angel blinked as she felt the immense
power of that smile—like a mule kicking blindly at her
heart.

Lorcan was grizzling louder now, so she bent over,
lifted him carefully out of his cot and studied him. He
was as tiny as a doll, with skinny little limbs and a face
which went scarlet as his crying gathered momentum.

'Shh,' she crooned gently, and when this had no effect
she looked up at Rory, silent appeal in her eyes, because
she was terrified that Lorcan would start rooting at her
breast again.

'I'd better go and heat this bottle,' he said, the sound of Lorcan's cry clearly making him uncomfortable.

It moved her to see a big, strong man like Rory held in thrall to a tiny baby. Her eyes followed him obsessively as she watched him leave the room, safe in the knowledge that he couldn't see her. She was aware that her eyes lingered too long on the black jeans which moulded the outline of his powerful thighs and buttocks, but she couldn't seem to stop looking.

And yet she was not a woman who normally analysed a man's physique, nor saw a man in terms of sexual potency. Since Chad it was as though that side of her was dead, if indeed it had ever lived in the first place. So was it Rory who was making her act out of character, or the situation she found herself in?

She was conscious of a subtle change in her behaviour and in her reaction to him. Of the fact that something unexpected and inexplicable seemed to have taken place. Had Rory woken in her feelings she had thought long gone? Or had her husband's tragic death affected her state of mind, even though her marriage had long been over? For didn't they say that people were at their most vital when someone had died—as if death reminded them keenly of life itself. Didn't the frightening finality of death make you want to snatch at all the best bits of living before it was too late?

How ironic, then, that the one man to provoke these unsettling feelings of awareness should be one who would be—by the very nature of her job and her relationship with him—strictly off limits.

Lorcan was screaming now, so Angel walked him up

and down, holding him tightly against her while she sang softly to him, but he was too hungry and too young to be soothed by comfort alone. He wanted food, and he wanted it *now*. When Rory came back into the room, holding the warm bottle, she swooped on it like a mother hen and he found he was smiling as he settled down in an easy chair by the window to watch her feed him.

It was peaceful there in the bedroom, with just the sound of the baby drinking, the fire spitting. The baby glugged on contentedly, and occasionally Angel would glance up to where the firelight gleamed golden and rus-set on Rory's skin, casting shadows which emphasised the slanted lines of his cheekbones and the strong, proud jut of his chin. She could not read any expression in the dark eyes which kept coming back to flicker over the tableau she made with the baby, and she wondered what was going on in that mind of his.

A man like Rory could look formidable at the best of times, but right now his mouth had lost some of its un-yielding expression, making it seem more approachable. Kissable, even. Guiltily, she withdrew the bottle from Lorcan's mouth and gently began to rub his back. The baby in her arms burped and Angel gave a delighted smile. 'Oh, you clever, *clever* boy!' she cooed, and Rory met her eyes in a moment of perfect understanding.

'Odd, isn't it,' he mused, 'how getting a baby to belch like that can give you the most enormous sense of sat-isfaction?'

'Maybe for a lawyer it's odd.' She smiled. 'But I've been a nanny—it's one of the highlights of the work-ing day!'

He regarded her with growing respect as she petted the baby. Yet as his admiration grew he found himself at fault, too, realising that for most of his life he had judged women solely on their material achievements. For the first time in his life he found himself discovering the devastating impact of a woman totally at ease with her femininity as she cradled the baby. He realised with a start that serenity could be *very* sexy.

Angel found his gaze unsettling. 'What time is it?' she asked.

'Getting on for six,' he said lazily, unwilling to move from his position of comfort. 'Why?'

Angel pulled a face. 'If the chef is anything like Alan Bollier—then I don't want to be late for dinner.'

He rose reluctantly out of his fireside chair and came to stand beside her, and Angel suddenly felt peculiarly vulnerable—especially when he held his arms out and it took her a moment to realise that he wanted the baby and not her.

'Why don't I bath him and get him ready for bed while you get changed for dinner?' he suggested, as she placed Lorcan in his arms.

Angel looked down at her dress, the black dress she had put on that morning, which seemed like a lifetime ago. 'Changed?'

'Well, yes.' He couldn't help himself. His eyes moved with slow deliberation over the slender lines of her body and he raised his dark eyebrows in a mocking question. 'That is unless you're planning on wearing those gloomy-looking clothes down to eat?'

'And that would be hypocritical of me, you mean?' she queried. 'To wear black?'

But he shook his head. 'Unnecessary rather than hypocritical,' he corrected. 'And pretty unattractive, to be perfectly honest.'

She wanted to tell him that she would wear what she liked down to dinner—that it was nothing whatsoever to do with him. And that she didn't care whether or not she looked attractive.

Until she found herself dazzled by the deep blue blaze of his eyes, and realised that would be an outrageous lie...

CHAPTER SEVEN

PACING down the corridor to the bathroom, Angel braved the resolutely ancient plumbing system of the Black Bollier and managed to extract enough hot water to run herself a bath. Then found herself wishing that she had at least brought some bath-foam with her, so that she could relax properly in a few scented bubbles. It was just unfortunate that the only thing the hotel had bothered to supply was a hard bar of carbolic soap. The kind that people used to wash their faces when they were trying to prevent spots!

So much for the Cinderella transformation scene she had conjured up in her head when Rory had looked at her so disparagingly back there in the room!

Still, she washed her hair as best she could and then, pink and steaming, and wrapped in a towel with the dark curls streaming like wet ribbons down her back, she padded her way back to her room.

Just in time to see Rory emerging from *his* room with a towel wrapped like a sarong around his hips.

Rory stifled a groan and wondered why he hadn't left it a little longer; he had forgotten how long a woman could take in the bathroom. Now it might look as though he had contrived to meet her half naked in the corridor, whilst nothing could be further from the truth. Hell, the last thing he wanted was to see Angel looking like that.

And the last thing he needed to think about right now was sex. He should be thinking only of his dead brother, and not about how much he wanted to tumble his brother's wife down between the sheets...

He attempted the use of humour to create a barrier. 'Well, if it isn't a real live mermaid!' he commented.

Angel was too flummoxed by the sight of *him* bare-chested to do anything other than stand there with her mouth open, until he said, very gently. 'Angel? Is everything okay?'

'Everything's fine! Wh-where's the baby?' she demanded rather shrilly, finding that anger was a very effective method of distracting herself from the almost indecent length of his legs.

'Sleeping.'

'So you were just going to leave him, were you?' she accused. *'Unattended?'*

'Hell, I'm only going to be just down the corridor,' he pointed out. 'And I knew you'd be next door.' He had thought she'd be safely back there already.

'But you decided to leap out of your room to try and frighten me?'

'Frighten you?' he mused. 'Why? Do I?'

He most certainly did, but for reasons she wouldn't even acknowledge to *herself*—let alone him!

'Hardly!' she snapped. 'It takes a lot more than *you* to frighten *me*, Rory Mandelson!'

'Does it really?' Rory's eyes were bright with unaccustomed laughter, and he wondered whether humour had been such an effective method of diverting his thoughts after all. Right now all it was doing was creating a rather stimulating line in teasing.

'Lorcan's in your room,' he said, looking forward to a long, relaxing session in the tub. 'I just hope you've left me some hot water?'

'There was hardly any there in the first place!' she objected.

'So I'm in for a cold bath, am I?' he questioned drily. Which was probably exactly what he needed right now.

Still Angel seemed to be rooted to the spot, unable to tear her eyes away from him. What a torso, she found herself thinking. Not an ounce of fat anywhere. And those arms...

'Angel?' His voice floated hazily back into her consciousness, and she realised that he had been asking her a question. She racked her brains to remember just what the question had been.

His eyes narrowed as he stared down at her in surprise. Just how on earth did she do it? Rarely had he seen a woman manage to look so pure, so untouched— her unmade-up cheeks as fresh and clean as the petals of a rose after a rainstorm. Cursing himself for his provocative and inappropriate remark, he opened his mouth to say something, then seemed to think better of it.

'Doesn't matter.' His voice was surprisingly gentle. 'Run along and get dressed now, Angel—you're shivering.'

'O-okay,' she agreed. 'I'll see you later.'

Breathing heavily, she rushed into her room, slammed the door behind her and leaned against it, until she had her feelings under control again. Or almost.

She peeped into Lorcan's cot to find that Rory had not only bathed him but washed his hair, too—now how had he managed *that* in the small washbasin? He'd even dressed him, and he now lay all warm and sleepy in a fleecy blue sleepsuit.

She bent over the cot. 'You're a fine-looking boy!' she told him. 'Do you know that?'

The baby fixed her with a bright blue stare and Angel's heart melted.

'But the question is, young Lorcan,' she mused aloud, 'what am *I* going to wear?'

When you lived in rural Ireland, you tended to find that your wardrobe requirements were not terribly extensive. Angel lived in jeans and jumpers most of the time, or a smart black skirt teamed with a crisp white blouse when she was on duty at the hotel.

Why, even on her wedding day to Chad—admittedly, at his instigation—she had worn a pair of old jeans. It had been one of those deliberately casual weddings which was supposed to cock a snook at tradition but it had ended up feeling rather empty and hollow because of that. Angel had decided afterwards that it was a pretty pointless exercise. If you didn't agree with something on principle, then why on earth bother going through with it?

Should she wear black again? But Rory had not dressed in mourning, and clearly had no intention of doing so. And sombre clothes would mark them out, make them even more of a curiosity than they already seemed to be.

She rifled through her belongings until her fingertips

came to rest on her one good dress. It was of knitted lambswool, in a soft dove-grey colour—muted and discreet.

She left her hair flowing loose over her shoulders in an attempt to disguise the fact that the dress moulded so closely to the shape of her breasts. She didn't want him to think that she was going out of her way to *entice* him.

She stared at herself critically in the mirror. With a glittering marcasite brooch pinned onto the collar then surely she would pass muster—even for a London barrister?

It was a long time since Angel had taken so much care in getting ready, and it brought her no pleasure to question why. *Should* they be sharing a delicious supper *à deux* at a time like this? Maybe she should have insisted on a tray in her room. Except, she realised, Rory would have probably talked her out of it.

She thought about make-up, then decided against it. Her skin was pink and clear from healthy country living and the lashes which framed her emerald eyes were dark enough to provide a dramatic foil. Her only adornment was the faintest slick of gloss on her lips, which made them look much fuller, even a little bit provocative...

She tried to tell herself that it was not a cardinal sin to wear a tiny bit of lipstick. This was, after all, her first dinner date in more than eighteen months.

And then the realisation of what she was doing suddenly hit her, and her legs seemed to give way. She sank down onto the edge of the bed and stared unseeing at the fire, which was how Rory found her when he rapped on the door about twenty minutes later.

He walked in with his dark hair still damp, his eyes narrowing fractionally as he took in her hunched stance and miserable expression. He immediately glanced over at the cot. 'Is Lorcan okay?' he demanded.

'Lorcan's fine.'

'Then what's the matter?' he asked her, very quietly.

His softness was her undoing, and she stared up at him, afraid that her bottom lip might start wobbling. 'Nothing.'

'Well, it's obviously something,' he contradicted, with the air of a man who had spent his life digging out the truth. 'Or is it just the thought of having dinner with me?'

Angel met that searching sapphire stare and felt all her defences disintegrate. There was nothing to be gained from feeling bad and just keeping it to herself, and she was a fundamentally honest person. 'It sounds so stupid...' she began falteringly.

He didn't react. 'Let me be the judge of that.'

'It's just that...well, I was really enjoying getting ready for dinner,' she told him, as though that explained everything.

Rory looked very slightly taken aback, and then rather pleased, but he had scant experience of women who were not ashamed of appearing vulnerable. And Angel looked very vulnerable right now. 'How very flattering,' he offered approvingly. 'What's wrong with that?'

'Everything!' she declared. 'Chad has been dead barely a fortnight—and here I am, worrying about what to wear...' Her voice tailed off.

'And?' he prompted.

'It just doesn't seem right, somehow—to be getting excited about going out to dinner, when Chad is…is—'

'Yes, I know,' he butted in, and his face tightened with an almost unbearable tension. 'I had to go and identify his body, Angel—remember?'

Angel flinched, her mind picturing the scene with sickening clarity.

'I'm sorry,' he added quickly, silently cursing himself for his insensitivity. 'But life goes on, you know.' He saw the expression on her face. 'Yes, it's a cliché, I know it is, but clichés are universal sayings which get repeated over and over because they happen to be true. Life *has* to go on, Angel. Sitting around with long faces and rejecting any enjoyment that life has to offer isn't going to bring Chad back, is it?'

'I know,' she answered miserably.

'It doesn't change the way you feel inside.'

'And do you feel hurt about it all the time?'

He shook his head. 'Not all the time, no. It comes and goes. Sometimes it overwhelms you and other times you can be feeling really good. And then you remember, and in comes the guilt.'

'That's what I thought.' She nodded slowly.

He looked over towards the cot. 'And what about Lorcan? Babies are very sensitive. It certainly won't help young Lorcan if we spend our whole time moping, will it? He'll pick up on it.'

'No.'

'Chad treated you appallingly to walk out of your life without a word of explanation,' he pointed out gently.

'He doesn't really deserve your loyalty. Or your sympathy—not really.'

Angel moved her head to stare into the fire, and her hair rippled with the dark red lights cast by the flickering flames. 'It isn't a question of what he does or doesn't *deserve*,' she whispered. 'I was just feeling sad, Rory. So sad. And a little bit guilty—perhaps if I'd been a better wife he might have stayed, and then none of this would have ever happened.'

It was difficult to tell which was softer—his voice or his eyes—as he moved to stand in front of her and held out his hands to pull her to her feet and face him. Suddenly they were close, much too close—as close as lovers—and Angel's breath constricted in her throat.

'You don't have the monopoly on guilt, you know,' he told her, quietly savage. 'Don't you think I feel it, too?'

Her green eyes were wide. 'But why on earth should *you* feel guilty?'

He shrugged, and the gesture only drew attention to the rigid tension in his shoulders. 'Because I could have picked him up from the airport—correction—*should* have picked him up from the airport. He asked me and I said I couldn't.'

'You'll drive yourself mad if you let yourself think that way,' she told him softly. 'There's no point at all in saying, "what if?"'

'I know that.' He sighed heavily. 'But that's human nature.'

'Tell me about it,' she urged.

His face filled with pain. 'I had a case on that day. A

very important case involving a wrongful conviction, yes, but I could have made it to the airport if I had just dropped everything.'

'So why didn't you?' she probed, understanding his need to put his feelings into words. And suspecting that he was the kind of man who normally locked these feelings away...

'Because I was still angry with Chad,' he explained, his voice a deep, low growl. 'And angry at the cavalier way he dealt with people.'

'People?'

'Well, you,' he admitted slowly. 'I guess I felt bad about the way that Chad treated you.'

Angel smiled, stupidly thrilled that he had actually thought of *her*. 'Well, you don't have to be angry on my account. I'm over it now.'

'Oh, really?' he queried in disbelief. 'Is that why you fled to Ireland like a bat out of hell, when the two of you broke up?'

'Where else would I go?' she queried softly. 'Ireland *is* my home.'

He shook his head. 'This bit isn't. You're miles from home.'

'Well, a big family can be cloying when you're trying to get over something—'

'And living the life of a middle-aged spinster is your way of getting over something, is it?' he accused.

Middle-aged *spinster*! 'Just what are you talking about?' she demanded, almost spluttering her words with indignation.

'I'm talking about *you*!' he retorted grimly, and Angel

got a good idea of how he must look in court. 'Carrying
trays from room to room like a wraith—'

'Who told you that?'

'Mrs Fitzpatrick. While you were packing. She
painted a pretty bleak picture of your life, if you must
know—'

'How *dare* she!'

'No dates,' he continued implacably. 'No outings.
Nothing!'

She opened her mouth in indignation, but no words
came out. There was nothing to say. He spoke the un-
varnished truth and her life had been empty of all those
things.

'Just how long were you planning to play the hermit?'
he quizzed quietly.

Angel let out a long, low breath. 'I hadn't really given
much thought to the future,' she admitted. 'I was too
busy licking my wounds.'

'And that was very sensible of you, Angel.' His smile
was determined. 'But those wounds must have healed by
now. You did your grieving for Chad when he was still
alive—so don't feel bad because you don't have the inclination or the energy to re-create those feelings now
that he's dead.'

'And maybe I'm re-opening those wounds by agreeing
to take care of his son,' Angel pondered slowly.

His eyes narrowed. 'Is that what you're afraid of?'

She didn't answer immediately, just stared straight
into the heart of the fire which glowed copper and titian.
'No,' she said eventually, 'I don't think I am afraid of
that.' She met his eyes with a clear and steady gaze. 'I

don't think I'm afraid of anything any more—but then, maybe that's just a reaction to what happened to Chad.'

'Death does have a peculiar habit of putting everything else into perspective,' he commented wryly, and then he looked her up and down with a curiously impartial scrutiny. 'And by the way, you look lovely.'

She looked at him suspiciously. 'Do I really? Or are you just saying that?'

He shook his head. 'Oh, no. I never say things I don't mean.'

She would have to remember that.

'So, are you hungry?' he quizzed.

'I'm starving!'

'Then let's go and eat.' And he swung the carrycot easily off the bed and led the way out of the bedroom.

The dining room was almost full, which, as Angel pointed out, was pretty good going for a heartless January night in the middle of nowhere.

Alan Bollier's mood was marginally warmer as he guided them to a corner table. 'I saved this one for you,' he told them grudgingly. 'It's quieter. There's room for the baby—or shall I put him in one of the back rooms for you?'

Angel and Rory exchanged questioning glances.

'We'll keep him here!' said Rory.

Alan Bollier grunted and handed them each a menu. 'The salmon's finished,' he informed them. 'But there are plenty of prawns. And some very good monkfish.'

Rory looked up. 'And the wine-list, please.'

'Do you want a decent bottle of wine?' demanded the patron. 'Or just plonk?'

Rory hid a smile. 'The former,' he answered gravely.

'Red or white?'

Rory looked across the table. 'Angel?'

'White, please.'

Alan Bollier grunted once more. 'Then leave it to me,' he said, and marched off between the tables.

'That man's a law unto himself,' was Rory's dry comment as he watched him go.

'He's what they call a "character"—and all Ireland loves a character!' Angel replied as she looked down her menu. 'Are we having something to start with?'

Rory began to relax. 'We most certainly are!'

The wine was brought to the table and opened. 'I'll let you pour it,' Alan Bollier growled to Rory, after they had both ordered soup followed by prawns.

Rory poured them both some wine.

Angel sat back in her chair and studied him as she sipped her drink. He looked tired, yes, though less exhausted than earlier, but even so he was undeniably the most attractive man in the restaurant.

But the reason he drew the eye had more to do with his presence than his rugged good looks. Because the air of quiet strength and authority he carried meant that there was real substance behind the compelling face and the virile body. A pretty dangerous combination, when she came to think of it! He seemed to have the ability to make a woman feel safe and protected while at the same time making her think about other things, too.

Things which certainly should not have been on Angel's agenda.

Like desire.

And wondering what it would be like to be locked in his arms and kissed.

Wondering too, why a man like Rory Mandelson had remained single all these years.

'You're looking very thoughtful,' he observed, his eyes narrowing perceptively as two steaming bowls of potato and leek soup were placed in front of them.

Guilty that she had been considering his lack of matrimonial commitment, Angel hedged. 'I was just thinking about how tired you look.' Which was not, in itself, a lie.

'Really?' came his mocking reply, and she could tell that he didn't believe a word of it.

At least the candlelight cast forgiving shadows which prevented him from seeing that her cheeks were on fire. She had thought that she was all grown-up now, and yet she could still flush with awkwardness, like the country girl she really was at heart. Food suddenly became a welcome diversion, and Angel dipped her spoon into the bowl, but then she looked up to meet his eyes and the soup was suddenly forgotten.

His gaze was irresistible. 'Were you thinking about Chad?' he queried gently.

Angel shook her head; Chad seemed like a distant memory right now. 'I was just speculating why it was you'd never married,' she admitted. 'But it's a very personal thing to be asking, and you don't have to tell me.'

He threw her a look of wry amusement. 'You certainly

believe in getting straight to the point, don't you?' he commented, lancing her with that inky-blue stare.

She didn't look away. 'People waste a lot of time saying things that don't mean anything.'

'So they do.' He sipped his wine reflectively. 'Well, for a start, I have an extremely busy job,' he began.

'So do lots of other men,' answered Angel immediately. 'And the world would be a vastly underpopulated place if that was the main reason for not getting married!'

He smiled, saw that she had barely tasted her wine and topped his own glass up while he considered her question. 'I guess the main reason is that I've never met a woman I could bear to have dinner with, night after night.'

Angel blinked. 'You mean—you've never found a woman attractive enough to want to marry her?'

'Oh, no.' He shook his head. 'Attraction doesn't come into it,' he told her gently. 'Attraction is easy—so is sex. It's enjoyable conversation that proves so elusive.'

Angel thought about this while they ate. It was a bit of an insult to all the women he had been out with. It sort of implied that he considered them good enough to share his bed but kept them firmly locked out of all other areas of his life. She wouldn't like that at all.

She noticed that Rory attacked his meal with genuine hunger and wondered how long it had been since he had last tasted food. She saw his shoulders gradually relax as the warmth and nourishment of the soup took effect, and she offered him another piece of soda bread, but he shook his head.

'I'll wait for the main course, thanks.'

Angel knew more about men than she sometimes realised. 'Eat it,' she instructed sternly, pushing the little ramekin of butter in his direction, and he obeyed with a look of smile.

'Yes, ma'am!' The bread disappeared in seconds, and he sat back in his chair with a contented sigh. 'That's better.'

'You look a lot better than when you first arrived,' she commented.

'Well, that's hardly surprising, is it? I'd done a lot of driving with a brand-new baby at the end of the worst couple of weeks of my life. And I took a bit of a gamble.'

'What sort of gamble?'

'Just that I came over with the intention of bringing you back to look after the baby—but I had no idea whether or not you would say yes, did I?'

'Oh, but you can be so persuasive, Mr Mandelson,' she mocked.

He smiled. 'And, to be perfectly honest, I can't remember the last time that I had relaxation forced upon me like this!'

'Well, maybe you should do it more often!' She let her gaze rove critically over his face, and she noted the fine lines which fanned out around his eyes.

'Maybe I should,' he echoed softly, without really hearing what she was saying. His brother's sudden, tragic death seemed like a distant dream right at this moment, and he wanted to prolong the absence of memory. He held his glass up to hers. 'So, what shall we drink to, Angel?'

Suddenly Angel's wise counsel deserted her, and she couldn't think of a single thing to say, growing more and more flustered under that penetrating blue gaze. And then the baby whimpered by her feet and she could have hugged him. 'To Lorcan?' she whispered.

Rory nodded, and his face lit up with both surprise and pleasure.

What had he expected her to say?

'To Lorcan,' he agreed, and drained his glass.

Afterwards, Angel could only remember fragments of what was said during the rest of the meal. It felt unreal; it *was* unreal—but mainly because both of them studiously avoided talking about the momentous tragedy which had occurred. It was as though they were both aware that a much needed meal could not be consumed unless the pain of bereavement was put on hold.

She knew that he told her about his legal career in some detail—but only because she had asked. And once or twice she managed to make him laugh with descriptions of life at the Fitzpatrick Hotel, and of some of the more outrageous demands that tourists were so fond of making.

In view of his tiredness, she had expected him to want an early night, but to her surprise they were among the last people to leave, and there was a definite thawing in Alan Bollier's attitude as he carried coffee and mints over to their table.

'He's cheered up, anyway,' remarked Angel, once he'd moved out of earshot.

Rory dropped a lump of sugar into his cup and stirred it. 'That's because we're sedately and respectably eating dinner instead of closeting ourselves upstairs and getting up to all kinds of mischief.'

Unable to give a smart reply to *that*, and unwilling to even try, Angel unwrapped a chocolate from its silver paper and popped it into her mouth instead.

They finished their coffee and went upstairs to their adjoining rooms, where Angel took the carrycot from Rory.

'He can sleep in with me tonight,' she said firmly.

'I thought I said that *I'd* take him,' objected Rory, but Angel could see that he was biting back a yawn with difficulty.

'He's staying with me,' she said again, as the blue-black shadows beneath his eyes drew her attention like a magnet. 'It's an ideal opportunity to get to know him.' And to make a complete and soppy fuss of him without Rory watching, maybe thinking that she had a hidden agenda, as some women did. During her years as a nanny Angel had learnt, to her horror, how babies could be manipulated like pawns. She had worked for rich, vain women who only ever touched their infants when they were sure they were being observed. Women who only play-acted the part of motherhood and didn't seem to care for their child at all.

'Please, Rory?' she finished quietly. 'Let me take him.'

He opened his mouth as if to object, but Angel pre-empted him.

'And anyway,' she chided softly, 'will you take a look at yourself? You're in no fit state to look after a baby!'

'And just what is *that* supposed to mean?' he asked her sleepily, trying to remember exactly how old she was. In the dim light of the hotel corridor, with her hair falling like satin around her face, she looked about eighteen, though logic told him that couldn't be so. She had been twenty when she had married his brother. 'Your euphemistic way of accusing me of being drunk, perhaps?'

'Drunk?' She eyed him up and down assessingly and almost laughed. She had grown up with men who could take whiskey in their breakfast tea! 'It would take a lot more than three quarters of a bottle of wine to make a man of your height and build drunk, Rory Mandelson!'

'Well, I *feel* intoxicated. Oddly intoxicated,' he murmured, and then he did something completely unexpected. He reached out to let his hand brush against her hair, and leaned forward to press his lips to hers.

It was a good thing that she was holding the baby, because otherwise there was no saying *what* Angel might have done in response. And maybe *she* was intoxicated, too—because why else would she want to answer that brief kiss by flinging her arms around his neck and crushing her body to his, clinging on so tightly that he would refuse to let her go? What kind of naive little country girl would allow herself to get so worked up about one innocent little kiss?

If he *hadn't* drunk wine, then Angel might have done exactly that. But the fact was that he *had* drunk wine—

not very much wine, it was true, but maybe enough to make him regret his impetuosity in the morning.

And besides, thought Angel, with a sudden shiver of acknowledgement, Rory struck her as a real man. The kind of man who might not want to stop after one kiss, and then what would she do? Would he not then find her out? Use his undoubtedly vast experience with women to expose her many weaknesses? Leaving her completely vulnerable in the onslaught of his skill.

She moved fractionally away from him and her silent refusal to let things go any further was obvious to them both. She shook her head, her hair shimmering agitatedly around the pale oval of her face. 'I think we'd better go to bed now,' she told him breathlessly. 'Don't you?'

He nodded. She had chosen an unfortunate way to express herself, but he resisted the urge to tease her. Although, on second thoughts, maybe a little joshing might relieve him of this unbearable ache he felt for her right then. 'I think we better had.'

Whatever else Angel had been expecting him to say, it had not been that easy capitulation. And, whilst she'd had no intention of letting him do any more than kiss her, she felt deflated that he hadn't even attempted to! Surely he could have put up a bit more of a fight for her than that? 'Goodnight, then,' she said flatly.

'Goodnight, Angel,' he whispered. 'Oh, and thanks,' he added softly.

She opened her eyes very wide. What was he thanking her for? For letting him kiss her? Or for not letting him continue? 'For what?'

'For everything.'

The way he said it touched her heart. 'Goodnight, Rory,' she answered unsteadily, and quickly took the baby into her room before her face gave her thoughts away. Or her second thoughts.

She put Lorcan's cot down and began to brush her hair thoughtfully. What kind of woman would be loved by a man like Rory Mandelson? she wondered wistfully as she got ready for bed.

Once she had settled Lorcan down for the night, she scrubbed her face, changed into warm pyjamas and got into bed hoping for sleep, but soon discovered why new mothers spent their entire time looking so white-faced and shell-shocked.

Because she simply hadn't been prepared for the fact that Lorcan would wake up every two hours on the dot. She had looked after young babies before, it was true— but she had never had such hands-on experience with one who was just a couple of weeks old.

A baby, moreover, without a mother or father. And, while Rory had told her that a baby of Lorcan's age was too young to have formed a really strong attachment— Angel simply didn't believe him. No matter what the books said, she would bet that he was missing his mummy.

But at least the long night gave her the opportunity to get to know him better—Angel slept as fitfully as the baby did. She normally thrived on a good eight hours a night, but, surprisingly, she found that whenever Lorcan woke she wasn't in the least bit grumpy or irritable.

She fed him and changed him, brought him into the big bed with her and stroked his velvet skin, using the opportunity to explore every inch of him. And as she examined each perfect finger which curled so tightly around her own she slowly began to understand that Lorcan was going to be much more than just a charge to her.

Because there *was* a bond between her and this tiny, defenceless baby—a bond far too complex to even begin to analyse—and Rory had been exceptionally astute to come to her for help, she realised. Had he gambled on her loyalty? Had he known that she would do more to nurture and protect this child than some anonymous nanny employed by an agency?

It was ironic, really—that Rory was getting from her all the duty and devotion of a wife, but without any of the bits which made being a wife worthwhile!

She pulled a face. Well, that was the theory, anyway. Angel had always found sex to be a pretty overrated activity. Oh, the build-up to it was exciting—no doubt about *that*—but...

The baby kicked his little legs and waved his tiny hands, and once again one little fist caught onto her finger and gripped it like a vice. She stared into his fathomless eyes, her heart going out to this innocent scrap whose whole world had been decimated by a cruel stroke of fate.

And, she, yes, *she* had it within her power to help make that world right for him.

'Don't you worry about a thing, young Lorcan,' she whispered to him through the tears which had suddenly misted up her eyes. 'Not a thing. For I'm here to look after you now.'

CHAPTER EIGHT

ANGEL was woken by a baby's cry and the morning light on her face, which made her wonder how she could have been so stupid as to leave the curtains undrawn last night. She struggled to free herself from the chains of sleep, and disorientation swept over her as she attempted to remember exactly where she was.

And then she did.

She sat bolt upright in bed and looked around the room as Lorcan's crying gathered volume and everything came flooding back like a tidal wave.

She was here at the Black Bollier Hotel, looking after a tiny baby. And Rory was here too.

Angel winced as the shocking memory brought with it the sharp clarity of pain. It was like a waking ritual that she had performed since she had first heard the news, her mind silently repeating the facts like a child learning tables.

Chad was dead; his lover was dead. Their baby was orphaned.

With a small yelp Angel shook her head, and unexpectedly pleasure danced into her thoughts in the aftermath of pain—unwilling and unsought, but pleasure all the same.

Startled, Angel looked over at the other side of the bed, wondering why she half expected to see Rory himself lying on the bed beside her, sound asleep, with his dark ruffled head on the pillow. And the reason for *that* came flooding back as well. They had shared the most companionable of meals, and the conclusion to the meal had been...

Angel swallowed. It had been no big deal, and yet... Had she simply imagined his lazy pleasure when his lips had brushed with tantalising brevity against hers? And the answering response in hers? Whatever the case, that brief kiss had been enough to ensure that her night had been spent fitfully—dreaming dreams of a disturbingly erotic nature. Dreams featuring a man with a stern, dark face and a strong, brown body.

It was already gone eight o'clock, so she slipped on a pair of jeans and a fleecy yellow shirt, then picked the crying Lorcan up. She wanted to spend time cuddling him, as much as she suspected he needed her to do so. But he was soaking wet and his hunger was too intense, his confusion too overwhelming. She contented herself instead with a quick hug before she changed him, then put him back into his cot, wondering whether Rory was up yet.

She yawned, wishing that she didn't have to go all the way downstairs. The first thing she was going to buy when she got to England was an electric bottle-warmer.

She picked up the carrycot and the movement seemed to soothe Lorcan as she stopped outside Rory's room and lightly rapped on the door. She waited there a full ten seconds, but there was no reply. Surely he wouldn't have already gone downstairs for breakfast without checking on his nephew?

She waited a couple of seconds longer and cautiously turned the handle—only to nearly pass out with shock. For Rory was indeed there, deep in sleep; he was sprawled out over the large, old-fashioned bed with careless abandon.

And he was completely naked.

It was last night's dream come to life. Angel stood, transfixed by the sight of him, too dazed to even begin to ask herself why her normal shyness had deserted her. Or maybe it had something to do with the fact that he was just so darned beautiful.

His skin was a soft, even shade of gold—except on the fluid curves of his buttocks, which he had obviously covered up with bathing trunks on sunny days and which were a rich cream colour. His back was broad, tapering down to a narrow waist, and it rose and fell gently with every slow, deep breath that he took.

Angel's own breath caught painfully in her throat as she let her gaze drift uninhibitedly down the rest of him, her green eyes alight with wonder. She had never dreamed that the masculine form could be made up of so many exquisite contrasts—hard, well-defined muscle and satin-soft skin and the crisp sprinkling of hair here and there. It was a body which an artist might have used as a celebration of life itself.

His legs looked so powerful, so brown against the rumpled sheets—with thighs which were as solid and as rock-like as stone…

Forcing herself to her senses, she was about to slip quietly out of the room when he stirred and she stood rooted to the spot, afraid that the slightest sound would waken him. Afraid that he would open his eyes and cast her in the unsympathetic role of voyeur.

He turned lazily onto his back, and this time she was certain that her astonished inrush of breath would tell him that he had an audience. And that her astonishment was due to the fact that he was fully aroused...more aroused than she had ever seen a man before.

Angel shut her eyes, but the image remained stubbornly in place, mocking her in her embarrassment, even though her reaction shouldn't have surprised her. Because her knowledge of men was abysmal. It had begun and ended with her late husband—something he had teased her about with ever-increasing venom. A few months into their marriage, and the virginity which Chad had so coveted had become the source of his scorn.

Angel opened her eyes and looked again at the proud magnificence of Rory's sleeping form, the obvious contrasts between the two brothers leaping to her mind unasked.

For Chad's body had not resembled *this* body. Not in the slightest. Chad's body had been pale and ever so slightly bloated, though he had always been obsessive about covering it up—even in the bedroom. But maybe that was because Chad had spent his long lunch-hours in wine-bars and most of the evening sleeping them off, or because his idea of exercise had been lifting up the remote control or a pint of beer. And it had showed.

Angel drew herself up in disgust. Oh, what in the name of God was she *doing*? Comparing one man to another—and in the most basic way imaginable? Was that the sort of woman she had become? Was she missing the sex she had gone without for so long? Was that it? Yet how could that be, when the intimacy she had shared with Chad had been such a crushing disappointment?

Cramming her fist into her mouth, she turned and left the room as silently as she had entered it, picked up the carrycot and made her way straight downstairs to the kitchen to heat Lorcan's bottle, her hands shaking like a leaf.

The kitchen was busy. Two women were heaping food onto plates for the breakfast orders—one bacon, the other eggs—and they hurried these on trays past Angel. A big-boned girl of about nineteen, all curly hair and freckles, was stirring a pot of porridge, her wooden spoon leaving a trail in the thick oatmeal. She smiled shyly at Angel and Angel smiled back—gesturing to the carrycot she was holding by way of explanation.

'I'm Angel Mandelson, one of the guests here,' she began. 'And I need to heat through the baby's feed.'

Thankfully, she didn't need to say another word, because the girl put her hand out for the bottle which Angel was holding. 'Give me the bottle here,' she instructed, 'and I'll do it for you. Why don't you sit down over by the door out of the way until it's ready? Then you can hold him.' She pointed to a chair in an alcove in the corner of the large room, far away from where the breakfasts were being assembled.

Angel was pleased to take the girl up on her offer, especially since Lorcan was now wailing miserably. She picked him up out of the cot and rocked him against her, but once again he began to uselessly butt his head against her breast. The girl by the stove sent her over a curious sideways glance.

Scarlet-faced, and embarrassed not to be feeding him herself, Angel felt compelled to explain, 'He isn't mine, you see—I've no milk to give him.'

The girl nodded, clearly mystified, but she knew what her boss would have to say if she began quizzing the hotel guests about their circumstances—especially on such a delicate subject and one who was so clearly embarrassed. She gave Angel a gentle smile and handed the warmed-through feed back to her.

Lorcan was hungry and scented the milk, squirming restlessly in her arms, and Angel couldn't deny him any longer. She placed the bottle to his lips and he began to drink hungrily while the freckle-faced girl watched curiously from out of the corner of her eye.

Afterwards, she put him over her shoulder and winded him, then put him back into his cot. She tucked the woollen blanket around him, marvelling at how quickly you could get used to the routine of having a baby, and went off in search of some breakfast herself!

The dining room was almost empty by the time she had settled herself by a window table, and Alan Bollier came over and greeted her with a kind of grimace which Angel supposed was a smile. Quite frankly, she was surprised he had any customers at all!

'Good morning! I'm not too late for breakfast, I hope?' she enquired sunnily.

'And what about your friend?' he asked immediately, peering up the stairs as if expecting Rory to suddenly materialise. 'Will he not be wanting breakfast, too?'

Angel shrugged. 'I've no idea. He's still asleep. I left him in bed—not wanting to wake him.' But as soon as she uttered the words, and saw the proprietor's disapproving scowl, she wished that she had expressed herself a little more carefully.

Now *why* had she made it sound as though she and Rory had just enjoyed a long and energetic night upstairs? As though she had left him spent and exhausted in his bed?

Not that it should matter, she told herself briskly. She was a free woman, for heaven's sake, and Rory was a free man. And this might be rural Ireland, but there weren't laws against people behaving exactly as they pleased, within reason!

'Is he now?' He looked at her questioningly. 'And will you be having the full fry-up yourself?'

'Yes, please,' Angel found herself saying, hoping she would be able to do the meal justice—otherwise Mr Bollier would look even more down in the mouth than he did already!

He went off to give the order, returning with a tray of tea, but Angel's attention was all on Lorcan, who had begun to whimper. Lifting him up, she prodded his nappy through his Babygro, but he was clean and dry. And she'd only just fed him. Which left only one need unfulfilled.

Comfort.

Rather self-consciously at first, she began to rock him and hum a little tune to him underneath her breath. She knew how important it was to talk to babies—and especially to this baby. She shuddered as she tried to imag-

ine the predominant sounds he must have heard in his
young life—the screams and the skidding, the sirens and
the sobbing. She hugged him fiercely to her chest, willing him to forget, vowing to fill his little head with pleas-
urable noises from now on.

Lorcan made a soft, cooing sound and Angel beamed
at him in delight. 'Well, that's a start!' she whispered
into his silken hair. She continued to cradle and rock
him until he dozed off in her arms and she was able to
place him back down in the cot.

The 'full fry-up' consisted of bacon, eggs, sausage,
mushrooms, tomatoes and fried bread—and would have
smelt delicious to someone who had been out working
the roads since dawn. But Angel found that she couldn't
stomach more than a sausage with an accompanying
piece of toast.

Alan Bollier knitted his dark brows together rather
alarmingly when he came over to collect her plate and
saw that she had barely touched her meal.

'You didn't think much of the breakfast, then?' he
wanted to know.

Angel looked him steadily in the eye. She really was
going to have to stop being intimidated by him! 'There
was nothing wrong with the breakfast,' she told him
stoutly. 'It's just that I don't seem to have very much
appetite.' And he could draw all the conclusions he liked
from that!

He looked down at her curiously. 'Is it just the one
night you're staying?' he asked.

'It is.' Unwilling to be interrogated, Angel quickly
picked up Lorcan's empty bottle. 'Would you mind if I

used your kitchen to sterilise all his baby equipment before we go? We need to make up some more formula, too.'

'No, I don't mind.' He stared down very hard at the black-haired baby. 'What happened to his mother?'

Angel looked up at him, her black curls tumbling about her shoulders. 'How do you know I'm not his mother?'

'Because I know who you are. I know old Ma Fitzpatrick, and if you'd been pregnant all this time, then I would have got to hear about it.'

Angel sighed, recognising defeat. She knew that this question was going to be asked of her again and again— she had seen the girl in the kitchen wanting to quiz her about the same thing. And, much as she might want to, she couldn't possibly keep evading or avoiding an answer simply because it was painful. For Lorcan's sake, more than anyone's, his mother's memory could not simply be brushed beneath the carpet like so much unwanted dust. Angel swallowed, the words heating in her throat like bile. 'She died. She was killed in a car crash. So was his daddy.'

It was the first time she had seen Alan Bollier show any emotion other than disapproval. Shock and disbelief darkened his weather-beaten face for a moment, and Angel saw him struggling for some kind of composure.

'Poor little fella,' he said eventually.

Did Angel imagine it, or were his eyes suspiciously bright as he looked at her? Did even egocentric men like Bollier cry over orphaned babies?

'You must come and go as you please in the kitchen,'

he told her gruffly. 'Help yourself to whatever you need.'

'Th-thank you,' said Angel, and, picking up the baby, she buried her face in his sweetly scented hair, for fear that she would do something unforgivably self-indulgent, like blubbing her heart out when she needed to be strong.

She breathed a sigh of relief as Alan Bollier took himself away and she was able to compose herself. She supposed that she had better go and waken Rory—for didn't they have a ferry to catch?

His bedroom door was still closed, but this time Angel rapped loudly, and she heard a muffled groan from inside the bedroom.

'Rory?' she called, wondering if she should leave him be.

Another indistinct sound.

'I can't *hear* you!' called Angel.

'How's Lorcan?' came the muffled question.

'He's fine.' She heard a movement from behind the door.

'Why don't you come in?'

'Are you decent?'

'Depends,' was the sleepy reply, 'on your definition of decent.'

'Clothed,' she shot back primly. 'Fully.'

'Hang on.'

Angel heard more movement and then footsteps padding across the floor before the door was flung open and there stood Rory, yawning, his long limbs still rigid from having just woken.

Angel avoided looking directly into his face, registering only the sweater he must have just roughly pulled on, judging by the dark disarray of his hair, and the jeans which were zipped but unbuckled.

So. No longer naked.

He avoided looking at her, too—his attention totally captured by the sleeping serenity of his nephew. His feet bare, he dropped to a crouching position beside the carrycot and peered inside.

'He's contented,' he remarked.

'I've fed him. And changed him. Winded him, too.' She didn't need to add that she'd cuddled him as well. After all, it wasn't as though she was in the market for Rory's approval.

But it seemed she had won it anyway, for when he lifted his dark head she could see the raw appreciation gleaming in his blue eyes. And the fatigue.

'Thanks,' he said simply.

Angel smiled. 'I was only doing my job.'

He shook his head. 'You were doing much more than that,' he disagreed, his voice deep and husky with weariness. 'What time is it?'

'Just after nine.'

'Hell!' he murmured, and rubbed the back of his hand across his eyes, yawning again. 'You should have woken me!'

'I just did,' Angel pointed out.

'Sooner.'

Well, that had been her intention earlier, but his unclothed body had put paid to that. There was a pause as Angel struggled not to let her embarrassment show, a

moment before she could allow her gaze to drift over
his strained face. The full night's sleep he had had only
seemed to have intensified his tiredness instead of less-
ening it, and she wondered if he had been as disturbed
as she had been during the night.

She stared at the blue-black shadows beneath his eyes
and at the laughter lines around his mouth, which had
been transformed by tension into deep ravines. His ex-
haustion was so extreme that you could almost reach out
and touch it, she thought, her self-consciousness forgotten.

'How long is it since you slept right through the
night?' she demanded.

He frowned, his face growing wary, then shrugged.
As if it didn't matter. 'A couple of weeks...' Ever since
the accident, in fact.

'Well, you can't carry on like this—you look like
death,' said Angel firmly, and could have bitten her
tongue off.

He gave a bleak smile at the cruel irony in her remark.
'Don't make me out to be a saint, Angel,' he drawled,
the slight tremor in his voice revealing his apparent care-
lessness for the sham it was. 'Fourteen nights of broken
sleep is nothing. Women do it all the time—sometimes
for months and months—*and* they're the ones who give
birth! I didn't!'

She shook her head. 'No, you didn't—but you had a
comparably traumatic life experience.'

He scowled at her. 'A *what*?'

'You've been traumatised—'

He made a small sound of disgust. 'Oh, *please*! Spare me! Don't come out with all that psychobabble rubbish!'

'You can call it what you will, Rory,' she responded sweetly, affording him all the patient understanding she'd used to give her dear old grandpa, who had completely lost his marbles towards the end of his long life. 'But you wouldn't need to be a psychiatrist to know that your brother's death has affected you far worse than you imagined.'

With a little click of irritation he picked up the sleeping Lorcan's carrycot, turned on his heel and walked moodily back into the bedroom, where, after a moment's hesitation, Angel followed him.

'And you haven't been able to grieve properly,' she continued inexorably, disregarding the forbidding set of his shoulders. 'Because you haven't wanted to upset Lorcan.'

With an exaggeratedly careful movement he placed the carrycot over by the window, then moved back towards her, his face dark with emotion—though quite *what* emotion, Angel couldn't have accurately guessed. Or even have wanted to, she thought, her heart suddenly racing.

'So what's your magic remedy, *Dr* Mandelson?' he demanded. His voice was distorted with sarcastic savagery, but by now Angel had enough experience of life and enough trust in her own instincts to know when a man was near breaking point.

'You need to let it out,' she urged him gently.

The contained man that was Rory Mandelson felt as though he had been thrown unasked onto a switchback ride of his own emotions. He shook his head in denial. What in heaven's name was happening to him? To the controlled lawyer who frequently had juries eating out of his hand, nodding their heads avidly, agreeing with every reasonable argument he put their way. Where was that man now? Teetering on the brink of a dark place he had no desire to visit, that was where.

He shook his head once more, the closest yet he had come to black, hopeless despair since his brother's tragic accident. And *she* was responsible, the woman standing before him now. With her wild black hair and her knowing green eyes and that pale, porcelain skin that looked too white to be natural. Witch.

'Let it out, Rory,' she urged him. 'Just let it *out!*'

He took her face between two hands that were trembling, shaking like an early-morning drunk's, gazing deep into her eyes, his own unseeing, as he let his emotions come pouring out in the only way that Rory Mandelson knew how. And that was by kissing her.

For a moment she just let him, her mind racing frantically as she wondered what to do next. How best to channel this overwhelming outpouring of grief. Because she could not push away a man who was crying out with silent need the way Rory was right then.

And anyway, in her heart she had known it was going to happen. Known long enough for her to have been able to put a stop to it. Long enough not to want to. But she had meant him to cry, not this.

Or had she?

Was it really his tears that she had desired? Wasn't *this* what she had been wanting him to do? Certainly since last night—maybe even since the moment he had walked into Fitzpatrick's yesterday. Maybe, subconsciously, since even earlier than that.

His hands had moved from her face to her hair, burying his fingers into its silky depths as though seeking warmth and comfort there. She felt his tongue plunder her mouth, his lips so hot and hard on hers that it was as if he wanted to consume every bit of her.

And suddenly Angel herself found that she was acting just as blindly, uncaring of the sheer foolishness of their actions as she kissed him back, rising on tiptoes to wrap her arms like an anaconda around his neck, and he swayed against her, moaning with both gratitude and hunger.

He didn't say a word; the expert thoroughness of his caresses meant that he didn't have to. On and on he kissed her, and then after a little while he was doing more than kissing her. A lot more. Angel shuddered with pleasure and her eyelids fluttered to a close, her fingernails digging frantically into his shoulders although neither of them noticed it. Unbelievable to think that this was happening—to *her*, of all people. And that she was letting it happen, *exulting* in it happening, even.

She had never been at the mercy of her body before, not like this. Dear God. Never like this. She made no protest as he slid his hand beneath her shirt to cup her bra-less breast. Her blood sang with violent joy and she heard him gasp as he came into contact with the smooth bare mound, the nipple peaking involuntarily against the palm of his hand as though it had been made for no other purpose.

His other hand was sliding elusively over her thighs now, making her squirm, making her want him. Really want him. She felt him slide the zip of her jeans down, heard its reluctant rasp as he eased the denim down past her hips, her panties following, and her knees buckled as his fingertip touched her with an intimate longing. Unfamiliar sensations began to bubble up inside her like a cauldron slowly coming to the boil as he slowly eased her panties right off.

He fell backwards onto the bed and pulled her down beside him, kicking his own jeans off impatiently and peeling off the sweater which he had put on only moments before...

'The d-door!' she stumbled muzzily.

'Mmm?' He gazed at her unseeingly, lost in a dark sea of emotion.

Angel had the presence of mind to glance up as he pulled her shirt off, to see whether or not she had closed the door behind them. And her relief knew no bounds.

For she had. Oh, thank God.

She had.

CHAPTER NINE

NAKED in Rory's arms, Angel trembled as he pulled her tightly against him, his powerful legs entwining themselves intimately with hers, his hair-roughened chest scraping silkily against her breasts. Raw, pure sensation flooded her where their bare skin brushed and touched, and she gave a little yelp of delight mingled with disbelief.

Oh! It felt so *good*. Better than anything had a right to feel when all he was doing was running his fingertips greedily over her naked body, exploring her with a sensual thoroughness which left her helpless on the bed beneath him, unable to do anything other than moan with pleasure. And the small sounds she made seemed to spur him on even more. Wordlessly he ravished her, and wordlessly she revelled in the pleasure of the sensations he was producing, leaving her to fleetingly wonder whether a different Angel Mandelson had been reborn in Rory's arms.

For if Rory was behaving like a man possessed, then Angel must have been caught up in the same enchantment. Why else would she be coupled so compliantly in his arms, her body taut and extended like the bow of an arrow, her arms stretched high above her head in eager anticipation while an almost unrecognisable Rory demonstrated a depth of passion which shook Angel to the core?

His eyes were as dark as blueberries, his black hair tousled like a lion's mane from where she had run her fingers through it. Now he was nuzzling against her breast, suckling there, his lips sucking on the rosy tip as Lorcan had attempted to earlier. The sweet poignancy of the gesture was not lost on her, even while a shaft of sweet pain forked through her body, her honeyed wetness making her move her hips distractedly against the heat of him.

Rory was lost, totally lost—thrashing around wildly in the most intense physical storm he had ever experienced. Even as a teenager, with his first sweet foray into the waters of sex, he could never remember it taking a hold of him like this. Waves of desire washed over him, leaving him helpless in their wake.

He realised that he had broken every rule in his own book. And the number one rule was that he scarcely knew her, not really. He had used none of his usual subtle technique either—employing language and looks as delicate instruments of seduction. Rory groaned. He wanted to stop what he was doing right now, and yet he knew that he was incapable of stopping. Something else nagged at his conscience too, but the involuntary movement of her hips beneath his drove whatever it was clean out of his mind.

He was so full, so aroused, that he felt he was going to explode with the pain and the pleasure of it. Something primitive, something completely outside his experience was controlling him now.

He levered himself up on his elbows to stare down at her. For a moment his gaze hovered on the fevered innocence in her green eyes, and he felt troubled by it. But he had stilled for no more than a second when his attention was caught by the sight of her breasts, pointing high towards him and creamy-white, flushed with rose and gold and the subtle hues of aroused skin.

'Angel,' he said brokenly.

Angel looked deep into his eyes and could not deny him a thing. She found her thighs parting for him, lifted her hips to accommodate him for that first hard, powerful thrust, as though she was the worldly-wise one and he the innocent.

And when he entered her it was the most overwhelming sensation of Angel's life, the scales falling from before her eyes. For the first time in her life she truly understood the meaning of two becoming one. Right at that moment, she *was* Rory, and he was her. The two of them seemed indistinguishable as he drove deeper and deeper inside her, and she felt tears of joy slide from beneath her eyelids.

Every millisecond was like an eternity to Rory; never had he wanted to come as quickly as he did right now. He tried everything he knew—his mind tried to capture the waft of cabbage cooking when all he could smell was the scent of her sex. He tried to imagine ice-cold showers when all he could feel was her slick hotness as she welcomed each thrust.

And now it was too late. Too late to do anything other than press his lips to hers as his body erupted in the most explosive climax of his life.

Angel almost fainted with pleasure as she felt the flicking of his tongue into her open mouth mimicking the way his seed pumped into her over and over again. She felt his shudder of surrender, the beat of his heart pounding on her breast, and she wrapped her arms tightly around him, feeling safe and strong, rejoicing in her feminine power to have this big man trembling so helplessly in her arms.

In the aftermath Rory lay bathed in sweat, suspended in time and space, before the temporary oblivion produced by his orgasm throbbed away and he was left with an overwhelming feeling of sadness.

He rolled away from her and shot her a glance, as if seeking to confirm what they had just done. Wrong. What *he* had just done. And to whom. Dear God—hadn't his brother messed her around enough? Well, Chad had been younger, more foolish and more disconnected. *He* should have known better.

Rory turned on his side, knowing that he had to face her, wondering why she was lying there, with that soft, beatific smile all over her face, when…when…

Angel shyly opened her eyes to find herself fixed in the piercing blue blaze of his gaze. Not one word had been exchanged—there had just been that kind of choked cry as he had said her name. She felt so close to this man—closer than she could ever imagine feeling with anyone else—and the word 'communion' slipped comfortably into her mind.

She cleared her throat. 'That was…'

He leaned up on one elbow, his face suddenly alert as he waited. 'What?'

'Wonderful,' she sighed dreamily.

There was a faint hissing sound as he breathed out all the air from his body, falling back onto the pillow to stare at the ceiling, feeling as deflated as his lungs. 'If you're going to tell such blatant lies in future, Angel,' he said bitterly, 'then you really ought to get better at faking it.'

Genuinely confused, Angel rolled onto her stomach, her hair falling down in damp strands over her shoulders. 'What are you talking about?'

'I'm talking about what actually happened!' he told her angrily, but he was angry with himself—not with her. 'Not about what you would have *liked* to have happened!'

Angel was starting to get pretty angry herself, but, more than that, she was still perplexed by his attitude. Why was he looking as though it was raining soup and he was standing there with nothing but a spoon in his hand? 'We made love—'

'You didn't come,' he stated deliberately, wondering if they had a different expression for orgasm in this part of the world. 'Did you?'

But the puzzlement which remained in her big green eyes and the implications which lay behind it made Rory's heart lurch in horror, and suddenly he despised himself even more. She didn't know. Oh, my God—she didn't *know*!

His brother's death was still too new and too fresh in his mind for him ever to believe that he could have thought ill of Chad, but all he could think was…You *bastard*, Chad…. You stupid, selfish *bastard*!

And then Rory drew himself up short, wondering what had given him the right to stand in judgement. Was he really any better? Because if Chad had never given a thought to Angel's pleasure—then had he? Or had he just used her to vent his frustration and anger over his brother's death?

Chastened and appalled, he scooped her against him and noticed that she was shivering—hell, her teeth were even chattering! He tightened his grip, momentarily paralysed by self-disgust as he felt the dampness of her cheek against his bare shoulder.

He pulled back the bedding and manoeuvred them both beneath it. She tried to bury her head in his shoulder again, but this time he wouldn't let her. She might want to act as if nothing had happened—and if the truth were known so did he—but they couldn't. The fact was it *had* happened, and there might be repercussions to face.

'Angel, I'm so sorry—' he began, but to his astonishment she turned on him like a wildcat. She punched him hard in the solar plexus, momentarily winding him—and he backed off from her warily.

'Don't you dare apologise to me, Rory Mandelson!' she stormed, her mouth a wide red slash where he had bruised it with his kisses.

'But I didn't mean for it to happen,' he gritted. Not like that.

Exasperated, Angel pummelled her fists against his chest, though judging from his facial expression this had less effect than her previous punch had done. 'I didn't exactly sit around all morning plotting it myself!' she returned. 'But it *did* happen! And the moment you start

looking all shame-faced and apologising to me as though
I was some pure and unsullied virgin—then that puts *me*
in the role of victim! And I'm not going to be a victim,
Rory—not any more!'

'No,' he agreed slowly. 'Of course you aren't.' He
wanted to kiss the long, pure line of her neck. He wanted
to play with her for hours and to give her what she had
never had before. But he was perceptive enough to recognise that his urge to do so might be motivated in part
by his own masculine pride. Now was neither the time
nor the place to show Angel Mandelson just what she
had been missing...

He shifted his weight slightly, so that his powerful
thigh hid the fact that he was getting turned on again
just by thinking about it... 'I guess you're not on the
pill?' he hazarded heavily.

Angel looked startled. 'No. No, I'm not.'

He bit back the recrimination he knew he had no right
to feel. Yet he had seen her check that the door was
shut, *heard* her muffled protestation, even. She must
have known that he had been out of his mind with desire—so why the hell hadn't she bothered to ask him
about contraception?

Angel was wondering the same thing herself, particularly as 'fixing herself up', as Chad had used to unsym-
pathetically phrase it, had been second nature to her during her marriage. Chad had been so *paranoid* about her
getting pregnant that he would never have taken a risk
like she and Rory had just taken. She knew that she
owed Rory some sort of explanation. She just wished it

was a more convincing one. 'I wasn't expecting it to happen—'

'So you said.'

'And so naturally I wasn't prepared!' she snapped.

'Well, what do you usually use?' he demanded vexedly.

The implication hurt, though she could see that she had no right to be hurt. Why shouldn't he jump to the conclusion that she was having sex all over the place, in view of what had just taken place? 'I haven't had cause to use *anything*, as a matter of fact! At least, not since Chad.'

Rory frowned, his mind trying to work out what that meant in terms of months...God, *years*, even... 'But that's more than eighteen months!' he declared.

'It's more like two years, actually,' she informed him quietly, without knowing why she did so.

Rory frowned. 'But Chad married you in the September, and left you the following June—'

'So what does that tell you, Mr Lawyer Man?'

'That...?' He screwed up his face in disbelief and stared at her.

'That Chad and I only had a sexual relationship between the September of our marriage and just before the Christmas of the same year,' she admitted slowly.

Which told him two things. Firstly, it confirmed his guess that she *had* been a virgin before she had married Chad.

And secondly, 'He must have started his relationship with Jo-Anne at Christmas,' he realised aloud. And at the same time had ceased all sexual relations with his wife—although, judging from what little he knew, it would not seem to be much of a loss. Not to Angel, anyway.

'Go to the top of the class!' Angel gave a hollow laugh. 'I hope to God that you employ a little more logic in the law courts than you're doing just now!'

He resisted the temptation to say that in the law courts he wasn't usually lying naked next to a beautiful woman who had just given him the single most sensational sexual experience of his life. A woman he was aching to possess all over again, only this time...

He did the cabbage and cold shower thing with more effect this time, then cleared his throat. 'There are some questions I need to ask you.'

'You're sounding like a lawyer now.'

'Maybe that's because I *am* a lawyer,' he bit out, turning his head slightly to look at her, and then wishing he hadn't. Because he was treated to another captivating view of her beautiful breasts. 'Shall we get dressed?' he asked, realising as he asked it just how preposterous it sounded.

'Okay.' She shrugged, trying to act as if nothing was the matter, and wondering whether she was managing to carry it off. Something wasn't right and Angel didn't know what it was. Rory seemed really *disappointed* somehow, and yet, by rights, shouldn't he be feeling a macho kind of triumph right now? She hadn't exactly played hard to get, had she?

But what had started out as need and become beautiful passion had turned downright ugly afterwards. And some deep-rooted fear prevented her from asking him why.

Was it guilt? she wondered. Because he had just taken his brother's wife to bed?

Angel forced herself not to behave shyly—after all, they had just been as intimate as two people *could* be, and the act of love had moved her in a way it never had done before. But maybe she was just easily pleased. She swung her legs over the side of the bed and stood up, and she couldn't miss the unmistakable tension which tightened his muscles as he caught sight of her naked body.

She pulled her yellow shirt back over her head and slithered into her jeans, running her fingers back through the mass of wild black curls in an attempt to tame them. Rory was climbing into his jeans with his back to her.

Inwardly cursing at the way Angel had just flaunted herself around the room, Rory sent up a prayer that his zipper wouldn't dig into him. Or worse. He could see the headlines now: 'TOP LONDON LAWYER CASTRATED IN IRISH HOTEL'.

He picked his grey sweater up off the floor, where he had obviously hurled it in his haste to remove it from his body. By the time he felt ready to face Angel with any degree of equanimity, he saw that she was bending over Lorcan's carrycot.

'Is he awake?' he asked hopefully.

Angel, too, had been praying for the baby to stir. At least with a squalling infant to deal with, she might be able to delay whatever dreadful questions Rory was about to ask her.

But Lorcan was sleeping soundly and contentedly, as

he had slept through that rather tempestuous union on the bed. Which left nothing else for it.

She turned to face him, marvelling that he could look so *unflappable*. As though he hadn't just…just…

He saw the colour rise in her cheeks and knew that he couldn't keep dodging the issue at stake here. 'Is there a chance you might get pregnant?' he heard himself asking.

Stung and humiliated, Angel lashed out at him. 'Well, of course there's a chance I might get pregnant, you big eejit!' she declared. 'There's always the chance of *that* happening if a man and a woman have unprotected sex—or maybe they teach biology differently in England!'

A muscle began to work in his cheek and Rory hung onto his cool with difficulty—it wouldn't exactly improve matters if they *both* started losing their tempers. Particularly in view of her astounding innocence.

'What stage are you at in your cycle?' he asked carefully.

Angel blinked back tears. This adult questioning by a *man* about her monthly cycle was way outside her experience. 'What kind of question is *that* to be asking?'

He actually had no idea. This was, in its way, as intimate as he'd ever got with a woman. Oh, he'd made love to plenty in his time, but never like that. He simply couldn't imagine that demonstration of wild passion with any of his women. Because every one of them had tried to be perfect. Sex had been planned between perfectly laundered sheets after removing expensive pieces of French lingerie. Those women never belched, rarely sneezed and not one of them, to his certain knowledge, had ever left any evidence of her periods around. It was as though they had all read the same book and were spending their lives trying to follow its rules. He'd certainly never asked these acutely personal questions before.

He extended his hand to try to touch hers, but she angrily shook it away. 'Just give me some idea of your normal cycle, will you, Angel?' he urged gently. 'Are you midway, or near the end, or—?'

'Sweet heaven!' exclaimed Angel. 'Is this how you carry on with every woman you go to bed with?'

Well, he certainly wasn't going to allow her to get away with *that*. 'Actually,' he informed her icily, uncharacteristically ignoring the implications behind his next remark, 'I cannot ever remember having unprotected sex before, if you must know.'

Angel blinked, unsure whether to be flattered or insulted by this piece of information.

'So?' he continued doggedly.

With cheeks as pink as a Wicklow sunset, Angel got out from between clenched teeth, 'I'm on day ten, if you must know.'

Rory pushed away the mild sensation of panic, trying to appear unconcerned. 'Day ten, hmm?' He swallowed. 'Well, that's…that's…'

Angel said it for him. 'That's about as bad as it gets, isn't it?'

'It means a long wait until we know for sure.'

'And won't that be fun!' exclaimed Angel with brittle brightness.

He looked at the stubborn little rise of her chin and a sense of his own responsibility took over. 'If you are— pregnant—' he spoke the word with difficulty, smiling a rather bleak smile '—with my child, then I will, of course, marry you, Angel. That is, if you'll have me?'

Angel stared at him speculatively. It had been said with the air of someone who had just uttered a platitude. Someone smug and smart and cute as a fox. Someone who wouldn't *dream* that their offensive offer of marriage would ever be turned down.

She leaned forward, so that her face was very close to his. 'No, I damn well will *not* have you!' she glowered. 'And I wouldn't have you if you were the last man on earth!'

'Angel!' he protested.

'Don't you Angel *me*!' she declared. 'I've already walked into one marriage because it was what was expected of me, what I had been brought up to believe was right! That you couldn't sleep with a man unless you had a gold ring on your finger! Well, look where that got me!'

From deep inside his carrycot, Lorcan began to stir.

'Keep your voice down!' whispered Rory urgently. 'You'll wake the baby!'

'It's a pity you weren't a little more concerned about the noise levels and waking the baby when you had me over there on that bed!' she returned hotly, and was rewarded with an appalled look of discomposure. 'And then we wouldn't have to be having this discussion in the first place!'

'Angel, please calm down—'

'I don't feel like calming down!'

'Then we'll discuss this another time—'

'But I don't want to discuss it another time. I want to discuss it *now*!' she shrieked, uncaring that she was bordering on hysteria, or what the guests in the adjoining rooms might be thinking. Angel had spent her whole life conforming to other people's expectations of her, and she suddenly found herself asking why.

'Okay,' he agreed, and took the wind right out of her sails. He suddenly felt oddly calm—the prospect of pregnancy no longer the calamity he had at first thought. Death was a calamity, not life. 'Discuss away.'

She cleared her throat. 'If I am pregnant—if I *am*,' she emphasised darkly. 'Then I will have the baby, of course—'

'I'm very pleased to hear it,' he interrupted gravely.

'And you will, of course, be allowed to see him. Or her.'

'Thank you.'

'And to contribute towards his or her keep, of course—'

'Of course.'

She met his eyes suspiciously. Was he laughing at her? Surely he couldn't be laughing at a time like this? She drew in a deep breath. 'Because I'm not going out to work if I've a baby of my own.'

He nodded his dark head. 'I see,' he said, consideringly. 'And why's that?'

'Because I don't want someone else bringing it up!' she declared, the memories of her nanny days coming back to her in a rush. Those rich, discontented women—

women who didn't seem to want their children near them, content to hand them over to an unknown girl from Ireland who did, in fact, grow to love them, but might so easily not have done. And she would never risk that. *Never*!

'No,' he said slowly. 'I can understand that.'

'You can?'

He registered the incredulity in her voice. 'Of course I can! You want them growing up with the values which *you* hold important, not someone else's. Someone else could put all the wrong ideas in their heads.'

It was spooky how he had put her thoughts into words so accurately. But it didn't change a thing. 'Which is why,' she finished proudly, 'I won't marry you!'

Rory wasn't quite sure how he felt now, being torn between exasperation and an overwhelming desire for this woman who was railing against him so passionately. Part of him wanted to regress to an old-fashioned stereotype—to throw her over his knee and spank her—whilst the other part of him wanted to do something very different indeed.

But if he was being brutally honest with himself her flat refusal of his proposal was the last response in the world he would have expected from *any* woman. And he realised that he had done Angel a grave disservice by imagining that because she had no high-powered career of her own she would have leapt at the chance of being married to him.

Some women, he realised, with a flash of sudden insight, could be strong and good and true whatever they did in life. Their lives could be a success in all kinds of ways, and they didn't necessarily need a job to define them.

He was unprepared for the sinking of his heart as it occurred to him what her refusal might mean. And not just in terms of having to find alternative childcare, either. She was feisty and unpredictable, but at least she made him feel alive. And he desperately needed to feel alive right now.

'Does that mean that you're no longer willing to come over to London with me to look after Lorcan?'

Angel stared at him as though he had just taken leave of his senses. 'And who said anything about that?'

'Well, I assumed...*presumed*,' he corrected himself irritatedly, wondering what on earth was happening to him. Assumption. Presumption. These were words which he had probably used every single day of his working life during a highly successful career—and this minx of a woman had driven their proper usage right out of his mind! 'I presumed that in view of what has just happened between us...'

Glad of the camouflage, Angel let her hair fall forward to cover her face as she bent to scoop the now grizzling Lorcan out of his cot. She cradled him in her arms protectively and waited until she had regained some of her composure before she could meet Rory's eyes. 'Well, you were wrong, weren't you?' she told him quietly.

He found himself smiling. He would have kissed her if he hadn't been able to imagine her furious response. 'Was I?'

Angel steeled herself against that look in his eyes. What had happened this morning was certainly not going to happen again. Once could be forgiven as emotions running high after a tragedy, and please God she wouldn't be so unlucky as to find herself pregnant. Twice would be something different altogether...

Angel swallowed, finding that it was easier to concentrate on less momentous issues. 'You were,' she agreed firmly. 'Completely wrong. And I don't think there's any point in discussing it any more, do you? Not at the moment.'

He couldn't have disagreed with her more, but he could see that she had him over a barrel. He found himself wondering whether he would get another opportunity to lose himself in the pink and white beauty of her body, but wondering was pointless—it just got him right back where he'd started from. Hot and frustrated.

Angel shook Lorcan's rattle in the air like a maraca. 'And if you want us to catch that ferry, then someone has to make up some more formula, and we need to make a visit to the shops.'

Rory got the oddest feeling that he had taken on more of a woman than he was used to handling. 'Shops?' he queried faintly.

'Shops,' she agreed impatiently, fixing him with a stern look. 'We're running out of nappies fast!'

CHAPTER TEN

IN THE end, Angel went out to buy the nappies, escaping into the soft, grey rain of the misty morning—mainly because she didn't want to face Alan Bollier, who had probably had his ear to the wall, listening to all the goings-on with Rory. Although actually he wouldn't have needed his ear to the wall—she had been yelling loud enough for the whole village to hear all the way down the main street. In fact, her mother had probably heard it herself, in the next county!

Would Alan Bollier give Rory an earful about their disgraceful behaviour? Maybe add a few extra quid to the bill?

But when Angel arrived back at the Black Bollier, she found the two of them in close cahoots, with Rory drinking coffee and the proprietor sipping a glass of neat Irish while Lorcan was tucked away on a seat in the corner of the bar.

Both men looked up as she came in, weighed down with two gigantic packets of disposable nappies and some wet-wipes. Her dark hair was jewelled with tiny drops of rain which glittered like diamonds on black velvet, and Angel found herself blushing when she met Rory's eyes. Remembering that he had looked at her like that earlier, when...

Constrained by the need to be polite in front of Alan

Bollier, she found that she felt curiously defenceless as she looked at Rory now. He looked different somehow, more vital, his eyes sparkling and a flare of heated colour running along his cheekbones. But she guessed, with brutal honesty, that a man *would* seem different if he'd just made the most mad, passionate love to you.

He was dressed entirely in black, and yet his clothes didn't seem to make him look as though he was in mourning. They only seemed to emphasise his towering height, the dizzying breadth of his shoulders, and she felt like an ant in comparison. Horizontally, she thought guiltily, they had seemed far more evenly matched!

'Coffee, Angel?' he queried.

'Yes, please!'

'You look cold,' he remarked, as he poured her a cup from the jug.

She shook her head as she accepted her coffee and sat down next to Lorcan, peering into his cot with a smile as she did so. 'Not cold. Just a little wet, that's all.'

'Ah, the rains of Ireland!' proclaimed Alan Bollier sentimentally. 'It's what gives the women their fine complexions!'

Rory smiled, agreeing entirely. Right now, Angel's cheeks were pure roses and cream, but it did not seem an appropriate time to tell her.

'I'm ready when you are,' he told her instead. 'We should just make the catamaran at one-forty-five if we step on it.'

'I'd rather miss it and catch the next one if it means driving too fast on wet roads with a baby,' said Angel anxiously.

The two men exchanged a look and Alan Bollier said, 'That's women for you every time, I'm afraid—take the fun out of everything!'

Angel glowered at him. 'It's what's called common sense, Mr Bollier,' she retorted pithily. 'And if it didn't seem to be lacking in the male half of the species then it would be a better world altogether!'

Both men roared with laughter, and Angel felt oddly triumphant, wondering just what was happening to her. It wasn't really in her nature to be regaling the bar with witty one-liners. By rights she ought to be skulking around the place, shame-faced at having given in to Rory like that upstairs.

And yet the reverse seemed to be true. She felt immensely *powerful*—with an altogether new feeling of self-worth. How was that? Could it be possible that sex itself could liberate you like that?

Maybe it could, she decided. Maybe it could. Only— and here came a clarifying flash of insight—it would depend entirely on the man. Another man could have made her feel cheap about what had happened between them today, but Rory had not. He had thrown the ball back in her court by offering to marry her if she was carrying his baby. He had given her a choice, and in doing that he had given her power.

She sent him a grateful smile and had the satisfaction of seeing a look of perplexity cross his face, but it was gone in an instant. 'Shall we go, then?' she asked. 'It's almost eleven.'

'Whenever you're ready.'

It was as wintry a day as could be imagined—the light

seemed to be fast fading from the sky already, and it wasn't even noon. The heavy fine mist of the rain blotted out the colour of the mountains, so that only their shapes reared up alarmingly, and the road stretched out before them like a snake.

The journey to Rosslare took just under two hours. Rory had booked two adult places, plus the car, on the catamaran. Lorcan would sit on their laps.

Angel raised her eyebrows as he handed the tickets over. 'And if I hadn't come back with you?'

He gave a cool smile. 'Then the ticket would have been wasted, Angel, that's all.'

She wondered whether a failure to get her to fall in with his wishes had occurred to him. Probably not.

Angel settled in her seat beside Rory and looked around her with interest, thinking how much had changed in the years since she had first made this journey as a twenty-year-old. Though then she had chosen to take the ferry, which was cheaper. And slower, too. The Catamaran accomplished the journey in just ninety-nine minutes.

The vessel was almost full, even though it was a quiet time of year. There were very few Americans, tracing their roots in the old country, and even fewer backpackers who were 'doing' Europe. Here and there middle-aged men on their way back to England to work the roads drank Guinness from cans. But they were in the minority now. There was little need to work abroad these days. Ireland was buzzing and booming with its so-called 'Celtic Tiger' economy.

They reached Fishguard at three-thirty, and if the day

had been dark in Ireland now every trace of colour seemed to have been sucked up by the winter sky. The roads were rain-slicked and black, with streetlights glimmering in pools, like muted spotlights.

Angel settled back in her seat, confident enough in Rory's driving skills to be able to relax. His brother had showed off behind the wheel, taking risks and cutting up the other cars, but Rory was the opposite...

Angel drew herself up short. She had said she wasn't going to do that. She wasn't going to compare the two brothers...especially not now.

Rory watched her shoulders bunch up with tension, and wondered what was responsible. 'Is it odd?' he asked carefully. 'Being back in England?'

She thought about it. 'It seems like an awfully long time ago since I was here. Another life, really.' She turned in her seat to look at his profile, which seemed momentarily hardened as it was illuminated by one of the streetlights flashing by.

'And what sort of life do *you* have, Rory, in England?'

He didn't answer for a moment. 'The basics you know. I have a demanding job as a barrister, specialising in legal-aid work—'

'So you help people who can't afford to help themselves?'

'In a nutshell, yes.'

'And were you never tempted to sell your skills to the highest bidder?' she wanted to know.

He shook his head, the conviction he had felt in his idealistic twenties never having left him. 'Never,' he answered, with a smile. 'I have a beautiful apartment in Wimbledon, and you can only eat three meals a day—'

'I know—and only wear one pair of trousers at a time,' she interjected with a smile.

'Exactly! I work long hours, but it's work I enjoy. As for leisure, well, I like to read and play the occasional game of tennis—though I can be persuaded into the theatre from time to time if it's a play by Arthur Miller.' His face fell into shadow as they passed another streetlight. 'Does that answer your question?'

Angel smiled into the darkness. Why did men always answer questions with a string of facts that never really told you anything? 'Not really. What about friends?'

'I have friends,' he answered.

'And girlfriends?' she prompted.

He sighed. 'Why do women always want to know about other women?'

'Oh, it's just something we're born with,' she replied sweetly. 'So? Are there? Girlfriends?'

'I have lots of women-friends,' he murmured.

'I'm sure you have, Rory. But that wasn't what I meant.'

'No? You're talking about lovers, are you, Angel?'

Just the thought of his lovers made her want to scream out her jealousy, but he would never know that. 'I guess so.'

'You mean has there been someone specific? Someone important?'

'I imagine that there must have been,' breathed Angel, and her throat suddenly became constricted, as though she had a fishbone stuck there. 'After all, you're thirty-four years old, and English men tend to settle down much sooner than their Irish counterparts.'

'Maybe that's why the divorce rate is lower,' he mused.

'I think that may have more to do with the church's influence,' answered Angel drily. 'You were saying?'

Rory smiled at her persistence. 'I fell in love twice before I was twenty-five, but I had the good sense to recognise that neither woman would have made a suitable life-partner.'

'Oh, I see,' said Angel slowly, thinking how *cold*, how *calculating* he sounded! As though life was a game of Monopoly! 'And since then?'

'Since then there has been one fairly important relationship in my life. Her name was Sarah, and you met her once, a long time ago.'

Angel racked her brains to try and recall the woman he had brought along to the register office, to witness her marriage to Chad. 'Wasn't she blond? And slim? Didn't she work with you?'

'Yes, yes and yes.'

'But you make it sound as though she's past tense.'

'She is.'

'Has it something to do with Lorcan?' guessed Angel.

'How very perceptive of you. Yes, it has something to do with Lorcan.' He could sense her expectancy and knew that he was duty-bound to deliver, briefly wondering why Angel was not the kind of woman you could fob off with vague answers.

'What, exactly?' she asked, in a low voice.

'Well, we'd been dating for about three years—'

'But you didn't live together?' she butted in.

'No. There didn't seem any need, really.' He saw Angel's mouth fall open incredulously and attempted to explain his position a little better. 'We both had busy jobs and busy, independent lives. Where those lives converged it worked very well, and you know what they say—if something ain't broke, then why fix it?'

'Is that what they say?' asked Angel faintly. 'So what happened?'

'When—' He swallowed down the acrid memory. 'When Lorcan was orphaned, Sarah thought it best that he should be adopted.'

She heard the unmistakable bitterness in his voice. 'But you disagreed?'

'How could I pass him over?' he demanded. 'How could I deprive him of the only family he had left?'

'A lot of people might have said that you were unable to provide him with the family he needed,' Angel told him brutally. 'Might have said that a settled, nuclear family was the best place for a little baby.'

'Do you honestly think that?' he challenged.

Angel shook her head. 'No,' she said simply. 'I don't, as it happens. But you shouldn't make Sarah out to be the big, bad wolf just because she put forward what a lot of people might have considered a sensible solution.'

He laughed, but it was a flat kind of sound. 'The baby didn't really feature at the top of Sarah's list of priorities, and, to be fair—why should he?'

If she had loved Rory truly, then she would have embraced his adopted son, thought Angel, but she said nothing.

'Once she saw that I was set on keeping Lorcan, then she offered to come and live with me and look after him.'

'And to marry you?'

'Well, that was the general idea, yes.'

'But you didn't want to.'

He shook his head. 'No.'

'Wouldn't it have made life easier?'

'Who for? Certainly not for me. If I'd wanted to live with Sarah I would have been doing so already. And certainly not for Lorcan. I didn't want her near him,' he told her, with sudden ruthless candour.

'Because?' she prompted, on a whisper.

'Because she didn't care for him. She had no feelings for him whatsoever. To Sarah, Lorcan was a burden to be tolerated, nothing more.'

'But a lot of women feel like that about babies at the beginning, Rory—even their *own* babies,' defended Angel. '*Then* they grow to love them. And that's okay. This soft focus idea of instant bonding may sell baby equipment, but it doesn't always follow naturally.'

'*No!*' Rory changed up a gear and the car shot forward. 'If my feelings for Sarah had been strong enough, then I could have coped with her initial reaction, helped her work through it—but it took the worst kind of crisis to bring home to me the truth. And the truth was that I was drifting along in a relationship because it was comfortable and easy and because it required very little effort on my part.'

'And bye-bye, Sarah?'

'There's no need to make me sound like the Marquis de Sade,' he objected.

'So it was an "amicable parting", as they say?'

'Well, no,' he admitted. 'I always think that's a bit of a misnomer. The parting made me realise how one-sided the relationship was—a parting can never be truly amicable if one of you loves more than the other. And if the ending of a relationship seems nothing more than an inconvenience—then it was never meant to be.'

His words were like a revelation to Angel, as though he had suddenly freed her from a burden she had not known she was carrying. She had never loved Chad, she realised suddenly, nor he her. Their marriage had been a mistake—and her virginity nothing more than a crude kind of bargaining mechanism. Chad had hurt her pride, not her heart. 'So you split up with Sarah and decided to come over to ask me to look after Lorcan,' said Angel slowly.

'That's right.'

'But, Rory, *why*? Why me? Just because I used to be a nanny?'

'That's just it.' He sounded baffled, but indignant, too—as though he wasn't used to acting on instinct. 'I don't *know!* I hadn't planned it. I had to ring you to tell you about the accident, and then suddenly, when I spoke to you—everything seemed to slot into place.'

'Was it because I was married to Chad?' she asked him quietly. 'And you felt that I would love the baby—'

'As much as you loved Chad?'

Angel shook her head. In view of what had happened last night it was important that he knew the truth, but she was aware that she risked his anger, too—because the truth was, in effect, an act of disloyalty. 'I never loved Chad,' she told him painfully. 'I realise that now.'

'I see.' He spoke almost absently, as though he were miles away, as though it was of little or no importance to him, and Angel felt a strange, lurching feeling of disappointment.

She must have dozed, then, for when she awoke her mouth felt dry, her forehead sticky, and her neck ached. She realised that the persistent noise she could hear was the sound of Lorcan grizzling, and guessed that must have been what had woken her.

Rory glanced over at her, thinking how unnaturally pale her face looked in the half-light, remembering how a friend had once told him that she had known the very instant of conception. As though some women had a kind of mystical ability to detect the momentous change which had taken place in their body. *Could* Angel be pregnant? Could she be carrying his child in her belly right now?

He felt his heart thunder in his chest, appalled at what he had done to her. And what he might have done to her. 'Shall we stop somewhere to freshen up? We could have some tea, if you'd like that.'

'I'd love that.' Angel yawned fervently. 'And I'll change the nappy as you've done all the driving!'

He laughed, unable to think of a single other woman he could tolerate spending such a long journey with, in such inhospitable weather—and with a baby in tow. 'Done!'

It was getting on for eight that evening when they

finally drew up to Rory's apartment, which was on the second floor of a modern, purpose-built block overlooking the common.

Angel knew Wimbledon only vaguely. She knew that the world-famous tennis tournament took place there every year, and that there were lots of pubs dotted all around the common. Aside from that, she knew very little. She had lived in the posher bits of Knightsbridge for most of her nannying time in London, and during her brief marriage to Chad they had shared a poky flat just off the King's Road.

As soon as she walked into Rory's apartment, her heart plummeted.

He flicked a switch on the wall, and immediately lots of concealed lights sprang on all over the place. There was uplighting and downlighting and tiny spotlights in the ceiling which were little bigger than grapes. There was a big lamp made out of wrought iron which blazed on top of a low glass table. The lighting had obviously been put in professionally, since it drew beautiful attention to the paintings which covered the walls, and to the white piano which stood in one corner of the room on the bleached floorboards. Angel glanced around the room doubtfully. It looked like the kind of room you saw in magazines.

Rory put the carrycot down. 'Come and I'll show you the rest.'

Dutifully, she followed him into a kitchen that looked like the control room of a space module, only bigger. Every gleaming piece of equipment was like a textbook illustration of next year's model, and the microwave looked as though it would challenge any electrical engineer.

He paused after switching on the kettle, leaning back against a stainless steel work surface which might have looked good in an abattoir, watching her from between narrowed navy eyes. 'Well? What do you think?'

Angel was used to big, scruffy kitchens. The kind where muddy wellington boots could be kicked off unnoticed in the corner and dogs could doze in front of ranges. Kitchens where something was always cooking, quietly bubbling or simmering away and filling the room with tantalising smells. She shot a worried look at the oven. 'I can't imagine anyone baking bread in *here*,' she told him.

'There isn't any need,' he responded with a slight chill to his voice. 'There's an excellent delicatessen on the corner.' He marched out, leaving her to troop after him. 'The bedrooms are this way.'

This was the bit that Angel had been dreading.

The master bedroom looked as if it had been borrowed from the set of a bad eighties film, with an obscenely large bed mounted on a mirrored platform. '*Very* macho-man,' said Angel, torn between slight nervousness and the urge to giggle.

'I just haven't got around to changing it,' he growled, wondering why she was making him feel so defensive. To be honest, he hated the bed himself, but had been unable to summon up the enthusiasm to browse through the decorator's catalogues. A bed was just a bed, after all—but now, stealing a glance at Angel's disapproving profile, he could see that he might have been wrong. And speaking of bed...

He turned to look at her. 'Angel?'

She knew just by the tone in his voice what he was about to say, but she couldn't exactly impose censorship on speech, could she? After all, it was *his* apartment. And, in truth, he had a perfect right to ask her.

'Yes, Rory?' she answered, trying to keep the resignation from out of her voice.

'What if...?' Unusually, his voice tailed off as he struggled to find the right words—he, a *barrister*, of all people! Though these were hardly run-of-the-mill circumstances, he reassured himself. 'We can't keep pretending that nothing has happened. What if you *are* pregnant?'

'Then we cross that bridge when we get to it,' Angel answered automatically, before clapping her hand over her mouth. 'Sweet Lord in heaven—I can't believe I just *said* that!'

In spite of everything, he laughed at the comic humour on her face. 'Why not?'

'It's the kind of thing my mother might have said!' she declared, and then her cheeks pinkened as she saw him thinking exactly what she was thinking. What if *she* was a mother?

Rory's systematic legal mind struggled to impose some kind of order. 'You know, we really ought to discuss—'

'*No!*' said Angel, with a fervour which startled them both. But if that tumbled session on the bed at the Black Bollier had done anything it had ensured that Angel would never again feel less than Rory's equal. 'What's the *point* of discussing it?' she appealed. 'If I'm not pregnant, then talking about it's a waste of time, and if I *am*, well, then everything we say will be hypothetical, because we don't know how we'll feel about it. Not really.' She looked at him, her green eyes frank and clear. 'I'm right, aren't I, Rory?'

That was just the trouble, dammit! She *was* right! 'I guess so,' he sighed as he led the way to the other bedrooms. And at least one question had been answered without having to be asked. Judging by the look on her face as she had surveyed the king-sized monstrosity, there was no *way* that she was going to share that bed of his!

The remaining bedrooms were painted variously in electric blue, scarlet and emerald. 'Which one does Lorcan have?' asked Angel faintly.

'He's been sleeping in my room,' admitted Rory.

'No cot?' she queried, trying to imagine one of the bedrooms freshened up, with bright paint and mobiles sailing in the breeze and friezes and cuddly toys. It was a little difficult, somehow—seeing as every room in the apartment had the uninspiring dimensions of an oversize ice-cube.

'Not yet.'

The bathroom was the apartment's one saving grace, Angel decided. It was pure movie star—with a sunken bath the size of a small swimming pool and lots of impressive-looking glass bottles lined up with the obsessive neatness which told of a professional cleaner.

'Like it?' smiled Rory as they arrived back in the sitting room from the opposite direction.

Well, she could lie through her teeth, or she could start as she meant to go on.

Angel screwed her nose up. 'Not very much, to be honest.'

Rory went very still. He was used to adulation. Lots of it. 'Are you *serious?*'

'Totally.'

'Care to explain why?'

Angel marched straight across the room to the vast picture window which overlooked the common and picked up a pleat of one of the drapes, holding it between her finger and thumb. It was made of fine silk the colour of clotted cream and lined with a thicker material in a soft pinky-grey. 'Look at this!' she accused, waving the material at him.

Rory frowned. 'Don't you like them?'

Angel mirrored his frown. 'It's not a question of *liking* them—they look wonderful! But they belong on the pages of a lifestyle magazine, Rory—or in the life of a bachelor who can afford to have them cleaned every few months.'

'So?'

'So you don't qualify for the latter category any more! You've taken a little baby on board—don't you realise what that means? What's going to happen when he starts crawling? Rubbing chocolatey fists all over that delicate pale silk?'

A horrified look appeared on his face. 'He isn't going

to eat chocolate until he goes to school,' objected Rory stubbornly.

The odds were that he most certainly was, but Angel wasn't going to argue with that *now*.

'Jam, then.'

'Ditto.'

Angel opened her mouth, but he spoke before she had a chance to.

'Lorcan will not be eating food while he's roaming around the place, anyway,' he said, screwing his nose up. 'All his meals will be taken in a civilised manner. He will eat at the table. Like I do.'

Angel didn't say a word. She knew all about new parents and their ideas. What their child would and would not be allowed to do. He would find out for himself soon enough that the road to child-rearing was paved with compromise!

'Do you agree?' he demanded.

'In theory.' Their eyes clashed as she moved over to the exquisite blue glass vase which stood in the empty fireplace holding several spiky pieces of thorned twig. 'And what about this? *Very* child-friendly!'

'No worries. I'll move it.'

'And the TV?'

He scowled. 'Ditto.'

'Fine.' Angel nodded her head up and down briskly. 'And once we've baby-proofed the flat, we'll have to think very carefully about other equipment.'

'Equipment?' He looked at her with a frown. 'What kind of equipment?'

'Well, we won't be able to have a nice big, old-fashioned pram so that we can sit him outside in the sun. It will be too big to lug up and down all those stairs, and I shouldn't think that your ritzy neighbours will take very kindly to having their lobby obstructed by a huge great buggy! In fact, whatever kind of buggy we *do* get one of us will have to be watching him all the time, since it's a communal garden, and we don't want him getting snatched, do we?'

There was a small, telling silence. 'And just what do you suggest we do about the many deficiencies in my living accommodation, Angel?' he queried heavily. 'Any ideas?'

'Sure I do!' She smiled brightly, knowing that her idea *was* a brilliant one, but aware that it was an even better diversionary tactic, to stop her from thinking about the question which hung so heavily over both of them. 'We go house-hunting just as soon as we have time!'

The property agent looked from Rory to Angel with slight bemusement.

'Er, just to verify a couple of facts,' he said, glancing at the half-completed form in front of him before fixing them with his smooth, professional smile. 'You don't want a property that is modern and you don't want a flat, correct?'

'Correct,' said Angel assertively, ignoring Rory's black look in her direction.

'You want a property south of the river, four or five bed, three reception—'

'With a garden!' said Angel.

'With a garden,' the agent recited obediently, before looking from one to the other. 'Any other requirements?'

'Close to a park would be nice,' said Angel wistfully.

'Close to a park.' He wrote it down and looked up. 'And you are—' He didn't say 'Mr and Mrs'. Not these days—not even if there was a baby with them. He'd been in the job for twenty years, but no one ever seemed to get *married* any more.

'Rory and Angel Mandelson,' growled Rory.

The estate agent beamed. 'Oh, I see! Then you *are* married?'

'No!' put in Angel quickly.

The agent began to look seriously perplexed. 'Brother and *sister*?' he enquired worriedly, trying not to look at the baby.

Angel was giggling as they pushed their way out of the office and into the urban greenery of Wimbledon Village. 'What must he have thought?'

Rory's pride was still smarting from the way she had jumped in with her horrified denial that they were married.

'I'm not in the least bit interested,' he growled.

'Why are you sulking?'

'I am *not* sulking.'

'Sure you are,' answered Angel easily.

He laughed, and wondered why he could shrug off the burden of grief so easily in her company. 'Okay, then, I am.'

'Just as long as you realise it!'

He slowed right down and watched the way she walked the buggy ahead of him. She was wearing a dark jacket and a pair of jeans. Just a normal pair of jeans, but they moulded each buttock really *snugly* as she moved each leg forward. Rory swallowed and lengthened his stride until he caught up with her.

'Aren't you going to ask me why?' he asked.

Angel looked up at him from beneath the brim of a green velvet hat which matched her eyes. They had gone out to buy clothes for Lorcan, but the hat had been sitting there, just *waiting* to be bought. Rory had insisted on buying it for her and she had taken great pleasure out of letting him. 'Why what?' she frowned.

'Why I was sulking.'

She stuck her nose exaggeratedly in the air as she repeated *his* words. 'I'm not in the least bit interested!'

Rory smiled as he took over pushing the buggy and looked down at the sleeping Lorcan. 'Shall we walk around the common?' he asked.

'Love to,' answered Angel, and bent over to pull Lorcan's blue bonnet snugly down over his forehead. 'His feed's not due for another couple of hours.'

'We'll be able to buy a pram when we get the new house,' he observed thoughtfully. 'And sit it outside, like you wanted.'

At that moment Angel could have happily hugged him, but she thought better of it; hugs had a habit of getting terribly complicated.

And besides, she rather liked the way things were at the moment. Life was good, if not quite perfect, though she didn't dare analyse what her definition of perfection might be. Because if she failed to define it, to admit it to herself, then surely she wouldn't be too disappointed if she never achieved it.

It was a fortnight since she had arrived in England on that bleak and starless night. A fortnight during which she had realised that she was growing to love baby Lorcan a little more each day. And realised that it was going to be very difficult to prevent herself from feeling the same way about his uncle...

The February wind whipped at their hair and cheeks as they strode out towards Wimbledon Common, and Rory shot her the occasional glance, thinking that life had a curious habit of not turning out as you expected it would. And then he thought of Chad, and a shudder ran through him.

Life, he thought suddenly, was for living. All that stuff about putting things off until tomorrow was so much nonsense, when everyone knew that tomorrow might never come.

A car pulled to a halt for them, and Angel pushed the buggy over the zebra crossing with Rory beside her, matching her stride step for step.

'Mind if I ask you something?' he asked suddenly, and Angel averted her face, knowing what was coming. If it hadn't been such an awkward topic she might almost have *welcomed* it—because the pressure of continually skirting round a subject was proving more than a little nerve-racking, in spite of what she'd said the night they arrived.

She gripped the handles of the buggy. 'Ask away.'

For a man who spent his life asking questions, this

one was proving tricky to articulate. 'Angel, this is very difficult for me—'

She stopped and looked him straight in the eye. It was difficult for *him!* How the hell did he think it was for *her?* When every morning she awoke wondering whether this would be the day—every twinge of her stomach making her think that her period had arrived early. The unaccountable elation when it proved to be a false alarm... 'It isn't easy for me, either, Rory,' she said quietly.

He drew a breath, wishing that none of this had happened. Chad's death. The subsequent lovemaking. Everything. Well, no—not quite everything. Not Lorcan. Babies were unbelievably hard work, no question. You seemed to spend your whole time stumbling round like a zombie through lack of sleep. But he wouldn't be without him. Never.

He just wished that he and Angel had met some other time, and that he was free to kiss that pouty rosebud mouth of hers without the swamping feelings of guilt and grief. He gave her a sad smile. 'When are you actually due?'

'Soon,' she hedged. 'Very soon.'

'Oh, come on, Angel,' he protested. 'What kind of an answer is that?'

'But if I give you an exact date, then it's going to be like countdown at Mission Control!' she objected, trying to get him to smile. 'Every time I go to the bathroom there will be a question in your eyes! Yes, there *will,* Rory! You'll be scouring the cabinet for the telltale sign of a half-empty packet of tampons!'

He burst out laughing. She was irrepressible! 'If anyone else said that I'd be pretty shocked.'

'I'm pretty shocked myself!' she admitted thoughtfully. 'It isn't the kind of thing I'd have said to anyone once upon a time.'

'So what changed that?' he wondered aloud. 'Not that I'm taking credit for it, of course.' Because it certainly hadn't been his unbelievably selfish brand of lovemaking, responsible—that was for sure.

Angel gave an automatic shrug of her shoulders, but she knew in her heart where the answer lay. 'When Chad died, I think.'

He was appalled at the sharp dart of jealousy which shot through him. 'Because you realised that you *had* loved him after all, you mean?'

She shook her head and a strand of black hair floated down from beneath the green velvet hat. 'No, Rory,' she answered quietly. 'I mean precisely the opposite.'

'Explain.'

She tried to choose her words carefully. 'I don't think I knew the true meaning of love then. I married Chad for all the wrong reasons—because I'd been brought up to view my virginity as some kind of prize, and because I was lonely in London. Having Chad around meant that I didn't have to think for myself. But no one was forcing me to behave that way—it was *my* choice,' she added drily.

'Go on,' he said.

Her eyes grew faraway with memory. 'When Chad left I felt angry, and empty. Oh, I didn't cave in straight away. I tried living some sort of independent life in

London, tried to keep up with the friends we'd both made, but my heart wasn't in it. And neither were theirs, if I'm being brutally honest. Without Chad, they saw me as less than half a person—and in a way they were right. Chad was the puppet-master, only he'd left without cutting the strings which still bound me to him. When I ran back to Ireland, I wasn't intending to stay...'

'But you *did* stay?' he prompted gently.

'Yes, I did. Because it was easy—if dull. Like I'd put my emotions on the back burner,' she confessed, realising that this man knew more about her feelings than anyone else ever had. Including his brother. 'And then, when you gave me the terrible news, it was like waking up from a living dream. And, yes, there was pain, but at least I felt that I was *alive!* I realised that I could waste my whole life in that same ghost-like existence. I grew up, if you like. And I decided that from that moment on I was going to be true to myself.'

Rory digested this in silence, his conscience growing troubled. Had he perhaps been guilty of continuing to see her as the malleable young Irish girl he had first met, instead of the feisty, beautiful and sensitive woman she had so clearly become?

But he had responded to her as a *woman*, not as a girl. Hadn't he? Responded impetuously and intuitively, it was true—but something way beyond his experience had motivated his actions. Dared he define it? To himself, if not to her?

'So I could have ruined your life,' he suggested uncomfortably. 'If you *are* carrying my baby.'

Angel's heart leapt with primitive pleasure when she

heard the husky way he uttered those possessive words, 'my baby', but she forced herself to remain in control. 'That's a little dramatic, isn't it, Rory?' she teased. '"Ruined my life", no less!'

Her insouciance was beginning to rile him. He felt like grabbing her and shaking her by the shoulders, or rather, that was what he told himself he'd like to do. 'You know you're taking the whole issue very lightly!' he told her furiously.

'Well, what else am I to do?' she returned. 'It's happened. It's what they call a *fait accompli*. There's nothing we can do about it now. And for the love of God will you please stop acting like you're the big, bad wolf and I'm the wide-eyed innocent—'

'Which is exactly how I *do* feel!'

'Well, don't! I knew what I was doing. So did you.'

'But I don't usually—'

'And neither do I!' she stormed back. 'But on some fundamental, unconscious level we each made a decision at the time, and we behaved in a way we wouldn't normally have done! So what? Humans do occasionally behave recklessly, you know, Rory—that's one of the things which makes us human. So now will you please wipe that ugly scowl off your face and take us all out for something to eat?'

And, as had happened several times since Angel had moved into his flat and into his life, Rory found himself momentarily speechless.

CHAPTER ELEVEN

ANGEL flounced into the dining room and sat down opposite Rory, who was feeding Lorcan among the debris of morning newspapers and various cereal packets. Her face was pale and her heart was heavy. 'Well, guess what? I'm not!' she announced.

Rory was miles away. His sabbatical was almost up, and his lack of enthusiasm for returning to work next week had been totally eclipsed by the excitement of having found the house of his dreams yesterday. And it was the kind of house he wouldn't normally have even *looked* at, if it hadn't been for Angel. 'Mmm?' he queried absently. 'Not what?'

'Not *pregnant*, of course, you big eejit!' she sniffed, and burst into floods of tears.

Oddly enough, for a man who had always regarded himself as an emotional control-freak, Rory was usually very adept at dealing with crying women. He dealt with enough of them at the courts every day. But a woman sobbing with remorse for having stabbed her feckless partner, or crying her fury at having been caught with half a kilo of marijuana distributed about her person, was entirely different from the rather touching spectacle of Angel, now weeping quietly into a paper hanky.

The question was, should he risk going over there to comfort her and putting down a half-fed Lorcan, who would inevitably scream the place down, or should he offer soothing words across the table instead?

In the event he didn't need to do either, since Angel had started to interrogate him in a way which was decidedly hostile.

'So I bet you're happy now?' she declared.

'Happy?' Happy didn't accurately describe the empty little ache deep inside him. 'Yeah, sure, Angel. I'm delirious.'

'But you've been let off the hook!' she wailed. 'Haven't you?'

Rory weighed up all the pros and cons of the potential situation. 'I suppose that's one way of looking at it,' he answered reasonably.

It was obviously the wrong thing to say. Angel sobbed with outrage, causing Lorcan to start a little, before recommencing his hungry sucking.

'Why don't you have some tea?' suggested Rory calmly, wishing he wasn't trapped by the baby.

'I don't want any tea!' she gulped, and started crying again.

He left her to it while he finished feeding Lorcan, deciding that such a torrent would be better out than in. Then he took the baby upstairs and changed his nappy, before tucking him down in his brand-new cot and switching on his musical fish mobile, purchased two days earlier. The good thing about *very* small babies, thought Rory, as he went downstairs in search of Angel, was that they needed very little in the way of entertainment. They might turn your life upside down and inside out, but at least they spent most of their time sleeping!

He found Angel in the dining room, where he had left her, still sniffing occasionally, but clearly more composed than a few minutes ago. He took the teapot away to the kitchen, made strong tea and hot, buttered toast, and when he came back he placed both in front of her.

'Eat,' he instructed.

'I don't—'

'Eat,' he repeated, feeling oddly protective.

She obediently ate a slice of toast, drank her tea and felt much better afterwards. 'I'm sorry,' she said.

'It doesn't matter.' He narrowed his eyes in the direction of her white face. 'Er, do you get like this *every* month?'

Angel stared at him, itching to hurl something across the table at him. How could he be so *dense?* So *stupid?* 'Of course I don't,' she answered sniffily, then sighed. 'This is different. It's been an emotional time all round.'

'Yes.' He continued to stare at her. God, he could have sat staring at her all day. The tears had dried already, and there was no trace of them on her face. She looked so small, and sweet and scrubbed and defenceless. And, if he was being perfectly honest, he *was* pleased that she hadn't fallen pregnant.

Oh, the strutting macho side of him would have been pleased enough, but didn't this news liberate them both? Weren't they now free to start all over again? Only this time maybe a few judicious brakes should be applied along the way. Like the purchase of some condoms, for a start, he reminded himself sternly.

Angel watched him from out of the corner of her eye, desperately wondering what was going through his mind right then, but feeling so wretched and vulnerable under the influence of rocketing hormones that she didn't dare ask him. If only he had put his arms around her or *something,* instead of sitting over there and studying her as if she was some microbe on a slide in some laboratory.

He sat back in his chair and sighed, wishing that he could take her off to bed right now, eager to make up for what had happened last time. He began to calculate when he could first decently make his move.

And then he stilled.

What the hell was he even *thinking* of?

After everything she had told him, he was now plotting her seduction like some Machiavellian monster. How could he even contemplate something so rash and ruthless?

Angel had spent her adult life being pressurised, first by Chad, and then by him. Chad had wanted her virginity and he hadn't wanted to wait, so he had forced her into a whirlwind and ill thought out marriage which she had not been emotionally equipped to cope with.

Whilst he—*he* had used passion to coerce her. Hell, he might as well have held a gun to her head—she hadn't stood a chance against his desire and his experience.

He wanted Angel very badly, that much was true, and he had no doubt that he could make her want *him* back. But he didn't want to *make* her do anything. It was about time that Angel Mandelson started thinking for herself, and if she wanted him, then she had to damned well come to *him.*

He looked up to meet wide emerald eyes you could

have drowned in, but he steeled his heart against the reproach in them. 'I'll clear up here,' he said easily. 'You go and take a rest, freshen up, whatever. When Lorcan wakes up, we'll take him out for a walk.'

Two days later, they exchanged on the house.

'It's got everything a family could possibly want,' beamed the property agent who had given up trying to work out just what the relationship *was* between Rory and Angel.

Even given the agent's own talent for exaggerating, she just happened to agree with every word. It was the house of her dreams. It had a big, tiled hall—with plenty of room for a hatstand—and a sweeping old-fashioned wooden staircase. The kitchen was large—even by Angel's standards—and in pride of place stood a range, back in fashion in England for the umpteenth time around.

There was stained glass in the doors and in the windows, and the rooms were tall and spacious. To the front was the common itself, and to the back was a lawn sweeping down to an overgrown wilderness of trees and bushes where a little boy could play happily for hours. It also needed a hell of a lot of work doing on it.

'It'll take *ages* before it's fit for us to live in,' she moaned to Rory that morning.

'Delayed gratification,' said Rory tightly, as he tried to avert his eyes from her skin-tight tee-shirt. 'All the books say it's good for the soul.' Though he now knew from personal experience that it sure wasn't good for the body!

The following week, Rory went back to his chambers with mixed feelings. Part of him felt bereft at the thought of leaving Lorcan all day, and, it had to be said—he was going to miss his days with Angel, too. He had been living a different kind of life these past weeks—walking with the baby, shopping and cooking. Slow, lazy days— and not what Rory was used to at all. It was going to be odd standing up in court again.

But the other part of him was relieved at being able to extricate himself from what had the potential to turn into a very tense situation. Playing house with the lovely Angel, but without one of the best bits.

Like sex.

Yesterday had been hell. Valentine's Day. The whole nation had been awash on a sea of red roses, extravagant cards and TV chat shows asking, 'Is Romance Dead?' without any apparent irony. He and Angel had acted as if nothing particularly special was happening, and consequently their usual ease with each other had evaporated. The only Valentines received had been one for Lorcan—in Angel's writing—and one for Rory himself, which was definitely *not* in Angel's writing. In fact, he didn't have a clue *who* it was from, and had said so, whereupon Angel had given him a frozen smile and shrugged, telling him airily that his love-life was none of her business.

Some love-life, he thought gloomily as he bent to give Lorcan a kiss goodbye and briefly contemplated what would happen if he leaned over and did the same to Angel. With that mutinous look in her green eyes he wasn't even going to *try!*

'You can oversee the builders, can't you, Angel?' he said.

Angel was still sulking about the Valentine card. 'I can probably manage that,' she said coolly.

He scooped up various swatches of material, and different books of paint colours and wallpaper samples from the hall table, and presented them to her as though she'd just won a prize.

'And you can choose the decor, too.' He smiled, looking unfamiliar and formal in a dark suit.

'For the whole house?'

'The whole house.' He nodded, with a smile.

'On my *own*?'

'Sure.'

'But I can't do *that*, Rory!'

He fixed her with a quizzical navy stare. 'Why not?'

'Because it's *your* house!'

'Okay.' He shrugged, and took the nearest book from her. 'Suit yourself. I'll choose. We'll have a purple kitchen—'

'Give me *that*!' said Angel, and snatched the book back.

She became totally absorbed in the decoration of the house. It was the first time she had ever been given creative freedom, and she found that she had a flair for it.

'That's lovely,' commented Rory one night after dinner, when she showed him the hyacinth colour she had chosen for one of the bathrooms.

'Thanks,' said Angel, pleased, and flipped a page thoughtfully. 'Of course, having enough money helps, although I think I could quite easily get the same effect on a budget!'

'Want me to set you a challenge, then?' he teased.

She shook her head. 'No, thanks!'

She had started taking Lorcan to a mother and toddler group, even though she wasn't strictly a mother, and he wasn't strictly a toddler. But she wanted to meet other women with babies, since she figured that the two of them needed people independently of Rory.

Because Rory had started introducing her to his friends. They were a mixed bunch, which included actors as well as other lawyers and a couple of people who worked in the city. The majority of them were successful, but the main thing they seemed to have in common was a shared sense of humour. They accepted *her,* in any case, even if one or two were bursting with curiosity to know the precise nature of her relationship with Rory.

Angel sighed as she watched him leaning over the crib that night. It was something she would have liked to know herself!

She had thought...

What had she thought?

That as soon as her period was finished, Rory would carry her off to the bedroom for a repeat of that ravishing seduction?

Well, she might have *hoped* that might happen, but to date she was still waiting.

She had been deliberately suppressing all the feelings of desire she felt for Rory, and once she knew she wasn't pregnant those feelings had all come bubbling to the surface.

And remained bubbling.

Angel couldn't deny that they had the kind of relationship where they could discuss *most* things—and once you had discussed the contents of a nappy with a man it took you onto a whole new level of intimacy—but, even so, she still did not feel brave enough or confident enough to ask him outright whether or not he still found her attractive.

She spent one afternoon making pastry and singing to Lorcan, asking herself if maybe the pregnancy scare had done just that—scared Rory off for ever. Though, come to think about it, once you stopped thinking about pregnancy in the abstract and thought about it in terms of another Lorcan it *was* pretty scary.

But she could spend her whole life going round and round in circles, torturing herself with those 'maybe' kind of questions and never getting anywhere.

Or she could take some kind of positive action and run the risk of rejection.

But the more she thought about it, the less she felt like doing something as crass as planning a staged seduction. You might be able to shrug off most of what you had been taught, Angel decided, as she splashed bathwater over Lorcan's tummy one evening, but that would really be asking *too* much!

Rory arrived home from work and asked her if she'd like to go out to dinner with a friend of his, an American district attorney who was visiting, and her face dropped by a mile.

'Just me and him, you mean?' she squeaked, nearly

scorching the collar of the darling little yellow romper suit she was ironing.

Rory hid a smile. 'I was hoping that his wife and I might be included,' he offered gravely.

'Oh! Yes, of course! For a minute I thought you were trying to set me up on a blind date,' she admitted, with a sigh of relief.

He was seriously tempted to carry her off to the bedroom and give her some idea what he thought of sending her off on blind dates, but, remembering his determination that Angel was going to have to assert herself where he was concerned, he bit back the urge and shook his head. 'You are about to meet Lorcan Senior,' he announced, and Angel blinked.

'You mean...your friend from law school that we... you...'

'*We,*' he corrected firmly, 'decided to name our... Lorcan after.' He'd very nearly said 'our son', but stopped himself in time. 'Yes, it is!'

'That's fantastic!'

He smiled. 'So, is that a yes, Angel?'

'Why, I'd love to! But what about Lorcan—little Lorcan, I mean? Who'll look after him?'

'My assistant is begging to babysit. She thinks it will give her untold influence if she befriends my son!' Their eyes met. It was the first time he had used the expression.

'You're going to have to pay me some wages, then,' Angel said flippantly, relieved to see the trace of wistfulness leave his face.

'I thought we'd agreed that you would just use my

plastic whenever you needed to,' he growled. 'With round-the-world trips excluded, of course.'

'Yes, but this isn't for Lorcan, or for food,' she explained carefully. 'I need a new dress if it's dinner in a fancy restaurant.'

He smiled, remembering when they had bought the green velvet hat together. He'd never gone clothes-shopping with a woman before; that one trip had had him quite hooked. And he'd rather like to have an input on her evening gown... 'Want me to help you choose it?'

She shook her head, suddenly and inexplicably shy. 'No, I don't think so. I'd rather get it on my own, thanks.'

There had been a reason for her refusal, of course. Admit it, Angel, she challenged herself, as she wriggled to slither the green velvet garment down over her hips. It's because you want to surprise him. Surprise him, and then...?

It was perhaps unfortunate that the only dress she had come close to falling in love with was made in almost exactly the same material and colour as her hat. It came to just above the knee, and had a fitted bodice and long, fitted sleeves. She stood in front of the mirror in the scarlet bedroom, and did a twirl to admire the gown.

There was no doubt that the green velvet set off her eyes, and that the design did more than justice to her figure. It was just unfortunate that Rory Mandelson was now going to think that she had a very limited imagination where clothes were concerned!

Lorcan Powers—or Lorcan Senior—was a big, delightful bear of a man, and Angel could see exactly why the two men had forged one of those friendships which neither time nor geographical inaccessibility could affect. His wife, Clare, was an eye surgeon—small, sparky and ferociously bright, but not a bit intimidating. She fell in love with the baby instantly. 'I want one just like this,' she confided to Angel, as she cuddled little Lorcan.

Lorcan Senior was overwhelmingly flattered that Rory's nephew had been named after him.

'That's a pretty big compliment to pay a man, Rory,' he told his friend gruffly.

'Not as big as the next one I'm going to pay you,' said Rory with a quiet smile. 'Would you do me the honour of becoming his godparent?'

Lorcan nodded, too choked to speak, and Angel was enchanted to see the two men throw their arms around one another and embrace like new graduates.

Rory introduced her simply as 'Angel', not as Lorcan's nanny, nor his brother's widow, though Angel wondered what he had told them about her beforehand. But neither pried, for which she was grateful.

They drove out of London, to a four-star restaurant on the river, and ate exquisite, over-priced food. Afterwards they returned to London, to Lorcan and Clare's hotel, and listened to a pianist creating pure fantasy before saying goodnight.

As soon as they arrived home, Sandie, Rory's assistant, sprang to her feet and switched off the television. 'How has he been?' asked Angel, wondering if she made the poor girl nervous.

'Brilliant! He took his feed about, um, an hour ago,' said Sandie. 'And now he's fast asleep!'

Angel smiled and went through into the kitchen to put the kettle on, expecting her to stay for coffee, but Sandie didn't linger—she said she didn't like driving after midnight, and Rory saw her out.

He loosened his tie as he came back into the sitting room, and sent Angel a lazy smile which did dangerous things to her blood pressure. 'Nightcap?'

Angel bit back her instinctive remark, which was to wonder whether they actually needed *another* nightcap, but she didn't want the evening to end, so she nodded instead. 'Yes, please. I'll just go and check on Lorcan.'

The baby was lying on his side in the glossy blue and white cot, his cheek all pink and soft, the dark, silky hair falling in little waves around his ear. Angel bent over to kiss him and inhaled the sweet perfume of his babyness. 'Goodnight, darling. Sweet dreams,' she whispered, and went downstairs.

Rory was standing where she had left him, thoughtfully sipping a glass of juice, and Angel didn't know whether to be disappointed that he hadn't turned the lights down, the music up and put a bottle of champagne on ice to hand. Although, on second thoughts, maybe she was glad that he wasn't Mr Smoothie, with a practised seduction technique.

Though why she was thinking about seduction technique, she really didn't know. No, that wasn't really very honest, was it? She'd been thinking about it for weeks now.

'What would you like?' he enquired. 'Juice? Coffee? Wine?'

'Gimme a slug of whiskey!' she drawled, and laughed when she saw his look of abject horror. 'That was a *joke*, Rory. And you're supposed to go, Ha ha ha!'

'Hmm.' He shrugged darkly. The problem being that he didn't feel a bit like laughing right now. He felt like…like… He shifted his weight awkwardly and held his glass up with a questioning look.

'Juice will be fine, thanks,' said Angel, wishing he would remove that sour expression from his face.

They sat drinking their drinks in uncomfortable silence. Several times Angel opened her mouth to say something, thought better of it, then shut it again. What was *wrong* with them tonight?

Rory wished he *had* drunk the champagne he had considered putting out but had rejected as being too corny. He sighed. She was definitely sending out come-and-get-me messages, no doubt about it—with her coltish legs sprawled in front of her—but he was damned if he was going to be cast in the role of Mr Masterful a second time around. Because he needed more from Angel tonight than the occasional pout and the highly distracting glimpse of her black-stockinged thighs whenever she crossed her legs.

Angel looked up into inky-blue eyes. She wished he wouldn't watch her like that. Didn't he know what it did to her when his eyes grew all smoky and narrowed like that? He turned away, and she was glad. Didn't he know that her hands were shaking so much she was having to sit on them in case he noticed? Didn't he realise that she had terrible trouble falling asleep these nights, and that when she did it was just as bad, because in her dreams all she could see was him...

'Rory,' she said suddenly.

He turned his head back to face her. 'What?'

She didn't know whether the time was right. Whether he had grieved enough. Whether he wanted her or not. Suddenly, somehow—it just didn't matter. Nothing mattered, except her need to tell him what she prayed he wanted to hear.

'I love you,' she heard herself saying.

He stared at her. *'What?'*

'I love you,' she repeated. 'You probably think I don't know what love is, but, Rory, I do. Oh, I do. Now, you may not want me on those terms—in fact you may not want me on any terms whatsoever, I don't know—but I needed you to know that...Rory?' This on a delighted question as, silently and swiftly, he pulled her to her feet and into his arms.

'Oh, Angel,' he groaned. 'My *Angel*!' He closed his eyes and whispered a prayer of thanks. He was shaken by the courage it must have taken for her to say that. He had wanted her to show him that she cared, yes, but Angel had done so with every fibre of her beautiful, generous being. She had offered him the precious gift of her unconditional love. And now he just wanted to be worthy of it.

'Not *want* you? My God—wait and see just how much I don't want you!' He slowly raised each of her hands to his mouth, his eyes never leaving her face. He wanted her close to him, closer than he'd ever wanted a woman before. He wanted to cover her and enfold her. But he wanted her relaxed.

It would be easy to slide the zip of her dress down. Too easy. And too easy to slowly undress her here, to make love to her on the rug in front of the roaring fire. Like the stuff of fantasies. But tonight he did not want fantasies, nor need them. *She* was his fantasy and he wanted to make it *real* for her. He did not want them waking cold and aching in the early hours, when the fire had burnt away and they were left shivering, to creep through into the bedroom and climb self-consciously into icy, unforgiving sheets.

Tonight, she wasn't going to leave his side...

'Come on,' he whispered.

'Where are we going?'

His eyes glinted in the lamplight. 'You're the one who usually has all the suggestions, Angel.'

'But tonight I'll leave all the suggestions to you,' she answered him, though she was shaken to the core by the look of pure longing on his face.

He led her to his bedroom, unable to hide his smile of pleasure. 'Please don't be scared, sweetheart,' he whispered, as he began to kiss her and then to undress her. He was going to take this very, very slowly...

Angel felt slightly puzzled when they lay down naked on the bed and he pulled the feathery duvet over them. Surprised that all he seemed to want to do was to hold her, very tightly, and to kiss her, over and over again— the sweetest kisses she could have imagined. And he began to touch her only when it seemed that she would die if he didn't, exploring her in places that were only for him, would only ever be for him.

His skin brushed hers, thigh to thigh and breast to chest. She felt the heat of him, but it was matched by her own heat, the matchless sensation of being led towards something...something...

She moved restlessly, but Rory ruthlessly leashed in his own passion as though it was some wild animal he needed to control. What was it about this woman? he wondered fleetingly. Who could make him tremble with just a pout of her lips? Who could entice him with a mere toss of her hair?

She began to run tentative fingers all the way over the flat planes of his abdomen, but he contained her, shook his head, held her hands captive above her head while he entered her with one agonisingly slow thrust, and then another.

Angel felt as though she would shatter, as though some enchanting knowledge lay within her grasp with each exquisite movement of his hips. She was on a steep leaning curve, rising and rising until she had reached the summit, and suddenly she *knew*, knew and understood perfectly. Perfectly. She sobbed out his name over and over again while his words of love cushioned the fall and held her.

Moonlight stained the bed with its ghostly radiance, and Angel lay stretched beneath the duvet while her senses revelled in the glory of what had just happened.

Their bodies lay tangled, damp and warm. She felt his breath on her neck; she smelt the sweet, heady musk that was his own indefinable scent. His fingertips rested on her cheek and Angel turned her head very slightly, kissed them, and reached out her tongue to taste him once more.

He laughed, yawned, and shifted his weight onto his elbow so that he could look at her, pleasure and satisfaction gleaming darkly in his eyes.

'Hello,' he said softly.

'Hello,' she said back, but she couldn't just leave it all unsaid, as though he hadn't just given her the most earth-shattering pleasure. 'Rory...'

'That's my name,' he agreed on a murmur.

'It was...' Her words trailed away, and she shrugged her naked shoulders in appeal. All the words which sprang to mind seemed hopelessly inadequate. She tried again. 'It was...'

He gave her a slow, lazy smile. 'I know what it was,' he agreed, and then his smile faded. 'I was a selfish lover in Ireland—'

'No!'

'Yes, I was,' he contradicted, but his eyes were both regretful and yet filled with an odd kind of wonder. 'It never happened for me like that before—that sensation of being totally out of control.'

'Is that what it was like?'

He nodded, remembering the unnerving sensation of having been totally in her power. 'And it wasn't just *emotional*,' he said, frowning as he tried to analyse it— to himself as much as to Angel. 'Or physical. It was biological, too. Some subconscious, procreative urge which made me want to fill you with the essence of me.'

Their eyes met. They were both shaken by his honesty, by the way he had stripped the words right down, so that they performed the essential function of communication.

'We don't have to talk about this again,' he said abruptly, 'because it belongs in the past. In fact, we don't even have to talk about it now if you don't want to, but—'

'No, it's never happened for me before,' she admitted softly, as she anticipated what he was about to say next. 'Never with Chad, and he was the only other man I've slept with. Chad always made me feel a failure about it.' She paused. 'That's why I couldn't bear to discuss it with you in Ireland. Why I blocked it out of my mind subsequently. It was too painful for me to confront. Plus, of course, I didn't know what I was missing.' She smiled at him, still slightly incredulous. 'Now, I *do*.'

He turned onto his back and stared sightlessly up at the ceiling. 'You must have thought that we had both demonstrated the ultimate in selfishness,' he groaned.

Angel knew that this was going to be difficult, but she also knew that it needed to be discussed. Just once. And then they could both put it aside. 'It wasn't that Chad didn't *want* to please me,' she said carefully. 'It was simply not on his agenda to try. He had battled and battled to take me to bed before we were married, and of course that sustained level of wanting something and not being able to have it is unbearably exciting. I think that the wedding night was a real anticlimax for him— if you'll excuse the pun—after all that expectation.'

She hesitated. Chad had hated talking about feelings;

maybe that was the way it was between men and women. Was she now saying *too* much? But then she looked into Rory's eyes and knew that her fears were unfounded.

'Go on,' he urged softly.

'I think that Chad was so blinkered, so hell-bent on getting me, that he didn't think through the reality of tying himself down to an inexperienced woman whom he didn't really love.' She gave him a rueful smile. 'And I *allowed* myself to be used as some sort of trophy,' she admitted. 'I'm not shouldering all the blame on Chad.'

'Oh, Angel,' Rory whispered brokenly.

Strong in the certain knowledge of his love, she shushed him. 'The writing was already on the wall for our marriage before he met Jo-Anne.' She gave a long, shuddering sigh. 'God, I hope the two of them are at peace together somewhere.'

'I hope so, too, sweetheart.' He looked at her with tenderness. 'I love you,' he said simply.

'Yes, I know.'

'Sweetheart?' Rory twisted a dark strand of hair around his wrist.

'Mmm?'

'Didn't you tell me in Ireland that you wanted to get the baby baptised?'

She gave a great smile of delight. 'I did, yes.'

'Well, then, hadn't we better go and see a priest about it?'

'Oh, *Rory!*' And she flung her arms tightly around his neck.

They lay in warm, contented silence like that for a moment, before she traced the outline of his lips with her fingertip, revelling in her new-found freedom to do so.

'As for *you* being a selfish lover in Ireland...' She shook her head as she saw him frown. 'Well, you weren't. No, I mean it. And I wasn't lying, Rory—it *was* wonderful, just the sheer intensity of it. It was hunger, it was grief—comfort, too—and so much more. And I felt elated by your passion, Rory, and by my own power. Okay, so I didn't have an orgasm, but it was *still* wonderful. Making love is about so much more than having an orgasm.'

Rory smiled as he began to lick her belly button, and beyond. He was about to do some rather wonderful things to her body which would make her wonder if she'd ever actually said that!

In the pews there was uproar as murmurs of confusion floated around the echoey church, and Angel's mother and her brothers looked at one another in bewilderment.

The priest sent them a forbidding stare down the aisle. 'If we could just have a little quiet, *please,* ladies and gentlemen! As I just told you, we *do* have a wedding service to get through.'

'Sweet Mother of God!' exclaimed Angel's mother, for the second time. 'I don't believe it! She's marrying another of those Mandelson brothers—and she'll have her heart broken all over again!'

'And we thought we were just going to witness the poor child's baptismal vows, Mam,' whispered her oldest son, Gerry.

'The baptism will follow on immediately from the

wedding ceremony,' said the priest. 'If the couple are now ready?'

Angel and Rory exchanged a secret smile. They had made their true vows to one another one cold January morning in Ireland. This was for propriety. And for Lorcan.

Angel sent a loving look over at her son—*their* son— for that was how she thought of him now. A bonny six months, he sat on Lorcan Senior's knee and kept lunging forward to try and pull a feather off Clare's scarlet hat. The baptism had been arranged around Lorcan and Clare's busy schedules, and they had flown in from the States just the day before.

'I want Lorcan to feel that he has roots that go deep and far,' Rory had whispered to her reflectively one night. They'd been lying in bed, just looking silently at the stars and thinking how lucky they were. 'International roots. Roots here, and in Ireland. And now in America, too.'

Angel understood. Roots which would in some small way compensate for the early loss of his birth-parents.

The priest cleared his throat and put on his most serious face, which he hoped brought home the importance of the vows they were about to make. Inside, however, he was delighted. Absolutely delighted. A surprise wedding, no less! He'd always thought that there was nothing better than a bit of drama to keep the church alive. And there would be a good feed afterwards, at that lovely big house of theirs on the common.

At the back of the church, Alan Bollier looked with interest at the book of names he had brought for the infant child, and read that Lorcan was from the Irish for 'fierce'.

He smiled. In Ireland 'fierce' had a slightly different meaning than in England—it meant proud, and passionate. He glanced up to where Angel, radiant in a simple white lawn dress, was now cradling the baby against her and and trying to catch his eye.

She had learned from Alan that, on the morning of their departure from Ireland, Rory had told him that he had fallen in love. Hence the glass of celebratory Irish! 'Though Rory wouldn't touch it,' Alan had added, 'Seeing as how he was driving!' They now wrote regularly, and Alan delighted in sending Lorcan funny little presents which people brought him from all over Ireland. Angel smiled down the church at him.

Alan Bollier smiled back. He hoped he'd live long enough to see the child grow into a man.

Lorcan Mandelson, proud and passionate.

But with parents like that—he would need to be!

MILLS & BOON®

Next Month's Romances

Each month you can choose from a wide variety of
romance novels from Mills & Boon®. Below are the new
titles to look out for next month from the Presents™ and
Enchanted™ series.

Presents™

THE PRICE OF A BRIDE	Michelle Reid
THE VENGEFUL HUSBAND	Lynne Graham
THE PLAYBOY AND THE NANNY	Anne McAllister
A VERY PRIVATE REVENGE	Helen Brooks
THE BRIDE WORE SCARLET	Diana Hamilton
THE BEDROOM INCIDENT	Elizabeth Oldfield
BABY INCLUDED!	Mary Lyons
WIFE TO A STRANGER	Daphne Clair

Enchanted™

HER OUTBACK MAN	Margaret Way
THE BILLIONAIRE DATE	Leigh Michaels
THE BARTERED BRIDE	Anne Weale
THE BOSS, THE BABY AND THE BRIDE	
	Day Leclaire
AN ARRANGED MARRIAGE	Susan Fox
TEMPORARY ENGAGEMENT	Jessica Hart
MARRIAGE ON HIS TERMS	Val Daniels
THE SEVEN-YEAR ITCH	Ruth Jean Dale

On sale from 9th October 1998   H1 9809

JASMINE CRESSWELL

THE DAUGHTER

Maggie Slade's been on the run for seven years now.
Seven years of living without a life or a future because
she's a woman with a past. And then she meets Sean
McLeod. Maggie has two choices. She can either run,
or learn to trust again and prove her innocence.

"Romantic suspense at its finest."

—Affaire de Coeur

1-55166-425-9
**AVAILABLE IN PAPERBACK
FROM SEPTEMBER, 1998**

CHRISTIANE HEGGAN

SUSPICION

Kate Logan's gut instincts told her that neither of her clients was guilty of murder, and homicide detective Mitch Calhoon wanted to help her prove it. What neither suspected was how dangerous the truth would be.

"Christiane Heggan delivers a tale that will leave you breathless."

—Literary Times

1-55166-305-8
AVAILABLE IN PAPERBACK
FROM SEPTEMBER, 1998

4 FREE

books and a surprise gift!

We would like to take this opportunity to thank you for reading this Mills & Boon® book by offering you the chance to take FOUR more specially selected titles from the Presents™ series absolutely FREE! We're also making this offer to introduce you to the benefits of the Reader Service™—

- ★ FREE home delivery
- ★ FREE gifts and competitions
- ★ FREE monthly newsletter
- ★ Books available before they're in the shops
- ★ Exclusive Reader Service discounts

Accepting these FREE books and gift places you under no obligation to buy, you may cancel at any time, even after receiving your free shipment. Simply complete your details below and return the entire page to the address below. *You don't even need a stamp!*

YES! Please send me 4 free Presents books and a surprise gift. I understand that unless you hear from me, I will receive 6 superb new titles every month for just £2.30 each, postage and packing free. I am under no obligation to purchase any books and may cancel my subscription at any time. The free books and gift will be mine to keep in any case.

P8YE

Ms/Mrs/Miss/Mr................................Initials ....
BLOCK CAPITALS PLEASE

Surname ....

Address ....

....

....Postcode................................

Send this whole page to:
THE READER SERVICE, FREEPOST, CROYDON, CR9 3WZ
(Eire readers please send coupon to: P.O. BOX 4546, DUBLIN 24.)

Offer not valid to current Reader Service subscribers to this series. We reserve the right to refuse an application and applicants must be aged 18 years or over. Only one application per household. Terms and prices subject to change without notice. Offer expires 31st March 1999. As a result of this application, you may receive further offers from Harlequin Mills & Boon and other carefully selected companies. If you would prefer not to share in this opportunity please write to The Data Manager, P.O. Box 236, Croydon, Surrey CR9 3RU.

Mills & Boon Presents is being used as a trademark.

MILLS & BOON®

Emma Darcy

The Collection

* * * *

This autumn Mills & Boon® brings you a powerful
collection of three full-length novels by an
outstanding romance author:

Always Love
To Tame a Wild Heart
The Seduction of Keira

Over 500 pages of love, seduction and intrigue.

Available from September 1998